BATMAN™

ADVENTURES OF THE DARK KNIGHT

CONTENTS

BATMAN

ADVENTURES OF THE
DARK KNIGHT

Written by Billy Wrecks

Batman created by Bob Kane with Bill Finger

Who is the Dark Knight?

Batman is the sworn guardian of Gotham City. Under the light of the Bat-Signal, he fights crime in the city by night, striking fear in the hearts of evildoers. He protects the innocent, giving them hope that justice will prevail.

He doesn't possess superpowers, but he is highly intelligent and resourceful. He has been called the World's Greatest Detective because there is no villain he cannot track down, no crime he cannot solve, and no scheme so twisted that he cannot untangle. He has mastered several fighting styles and made his body very strong, becoming a formidable opponent for anyone who would dare to face him.

In his constant crusade against crime, Batman has armed himself with the most advanced high-tech equipment, including the amazing rocket-powered car, the Batmobile. He has also assembled and trained a team of allies, such as Robin and

Batgirl. Together, they fight villains as
different and deadly as the crime boss
Penguin, the eco-terrorist Poison Ivy,
and, perhaps Batman's greatest foe, the
insane Joker.

As the Dark Knight, he stands against
any and all threats to his city, and he always
prevails in his battle against evil.

Becoming Batman

The Wayne family had been prominent citizens of Gotham City for several generations. Over the years, the family business, Wayne Enterprises, became a billion-dollar company with interests in shipping, technology, defense, and other money-making ventures around the globe. While most family members were content to help run the business, one heir to the fortune, Thomas Wayne, decided to devote his life to helping others. He wanted to do more than just make money— he wanted to make the world a better place.

Thomas and his wife, Martha, had a son named Bruce. Being a Wayne, the boy had the very best that life had to offer and parents who loved him. Until he was about eight years old, Bruce Wayne was possibly the happiest boy in Gotham City.

Then one evening, Thomas Wayne took Bruce and Martha downtown to watch a movie. Outside the theater, a mugger stepped from the shadows and demanded their valuables. The thief's gun fired twice as he tried to grab Martha's pearl necklace. The boy watched in horror as his dying parents crumpled to the ground.

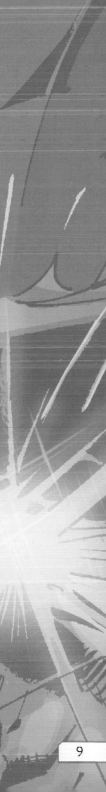

In that one dark moment, Bruce Wayne's parents were taken away from him and his life was changed forever.

Bruce wanted to save others from the horror that he had faced. However, he wanted to do more than just fight crime and injustice, and he vowed to fight the evil engulfing Gotham City. To do that, he realized he would have to train his mind and body to the peak of perfection. He would become a weapon against the things he hated.

Deciding to leave his pampered life of wealth and privilege behind, he sought out the people who could teach him. In the

Himalayan Mountains, he studied martial arts with the warrior monk Shihan Matsuda, which taught him superior fighting skills and strict control of his body. Another mentor, the brilliant engineer Sergei Alexandrov, helped Bruce master several scientific disciplines.

When Matsuda was killed, it made Bruce even more determined to continue on the path he had chosen. For several years, he traveled across the world mastering gymnastics, detective skills, disguise, and any other talents that would help him in his coming war against the gathering forces of darkness.

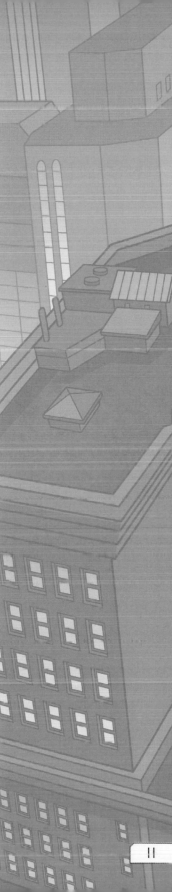

After years of intense training, Bruce Wayne returned to Gotham City. He felt ready, but his first attempts at fighting crime left him bruised and battered. Bruce quickly realized that he would have to be more than just a man to truly strike fear into the hearts of the city's evildoers—especially the new and frightening breed of criminals, such as the Red Hood Gang.

One night, while recovering from an unsuccessful fight against that gang, Bruce stumbled into his father's study, where he discovered a hologram that projected a terrifying image of screeching, swarming bats. Bruce realized that the bat was the symbol he needed to tackle the city's corruption and villainy.

He created a suit with a bat-like cape and cowl to conceal his identity. When he leapt from the shadows, the suit created the impression of a dark, monstrous bat. As he hoped, rumors quickly spread in the superstitious underworld that a creature of the night was preying on the wicked. They began to be afraid, and what they feared, they called...
Batman.

NEWS FLASH!

BAT ATTACK!

Report by
VICKI VALE

For quite some time, the mean streets of Gotham City have been no place for ordinary citizens to walk safely at night. However, are things about to get better... or a lot worse?

The *Gazette* spoke to Walter Rubinstein, a longtime Gotham City resident who was minding his own business yesterday, when he witnessed something amazing. "Three kids were robbing an apartment, as bold as you'd like," said Mr. Rubinstein. "I was about to call the police, when suddenly this figure appeared out of nowhere. Here's the crazy thing—he was dressed like some sort of bat! Three against one, but this guy beat them all. Shame he couldn't save the TV they'd nabbed from getting smashed."

So it seems our fair city may have a new resident— a "Batman." However, is he a force for good or evil? Only time will tell.

Personality and abilities

Bruce Wayne was born with a genius-level intellect, but it was his parents' brutal murder that gave him the focus to become an expert in the many disciplines he would need to become Batman. His desire to protect the innocent

and see the wicked punished has given him a strong sense of purpose and a will to succeed that borders on superhuman.

Bruce honed his brilliant mind during four years at college, where he studied a range of subjects, including mathematics, chemistry, computer science, engineering, forensics, and law. By applying this vast knowledge, he is able to outthink his foes and defeat them.

When he needs to stake out places where Batman or Bruce Wayne would be noticed, he uses his skills as a master of disguise. He often poses as the gangster Matches Malone to infiltrate criminal organizations and gain valuable information while undercover.

Batman is regarded as the World's Greatest Detective. A combination of intelligence and intuition allows him to recognize patterns, solve intricate problems and predict villains' moves. Only a few, such as the devious Rā's al Ghūl or the chaotic-minded Joker have managed to outmaneuver him, at least in the short term.

Batman's photographic memory allows him to recall everything he sees with absolute clarity. He makes observations, finds clues that others overlook, and goes over details repeatedly in his mind until the answers to his questions fall into place.

To aid his crime fighting, Batman uses the resources available to him through Wayne Enterprises to furnish his secret lair with the most advanced computers and the best laboratory equipment. His computers are linked to every law enforcement agency in the world, meaning that he can keep track of criminals no matter where they lurk.

Batman has perfected his body, just as he has perfected his mind. A regime of intense exercise, strict diet, and combat practice keep him at the very pinnacle of physical development equal to—if not surpassing—that of an Olympic athlete.

Batman is able to lift more than 1000lb (453.6kg). He can scale the sides of buildings, and has the agility to leap from rooftop to rooftop with ease. His impressive reflexes are lightning quick, he can run 30mph (48.3kph), and he can hold his breath underwater for almost four minutes.

Although the Dark Knight will use all his abilities, and every weapon at his disposal, to subdue an enemy, he will never kill.

He often combines many fighting techniques at once so that his foe can't predict his actions. He also uses several types of weapons such as swords, blades, and batons, but never a gun.

Batman knows that he has to be in peak condition—mentally and physically—to face any enemy that menaces Gotham City.

Armed and dangerous

Batman's suit does much more than just create the image of a large bat to scare his enemies. Like everything in his arsenal, the Batsuit has many functions. Most importantly, the cowl protects his secret identity. However, it also contains communication equipment, high-tech devices that enhance hearing and vision, and filters to screen out toxic gases.

The suit itself is made of titanium and Kevlar weave. It protects Batman's body

from injury by bullets, punches, and fire. His armbands have retractable blades for defense, and his cape can be used as a glider— handy when patrolling high above the streets of Gotham City.

Batman has also created other specialized suits to be used in different environments. One version is designed for high-altitude missions, while another is used underwater, and he even has a stealth suit that makes him invisible! Thermal versions of the Batsuit allow him to fight super-cold villains like Mr. Freeze or hot-tempered criminals who can produce incredible heat, such as Firefly.

Batman continually updates his suits with the most advanced technology available, to ensure that he always stays one step ahead of his enemies.

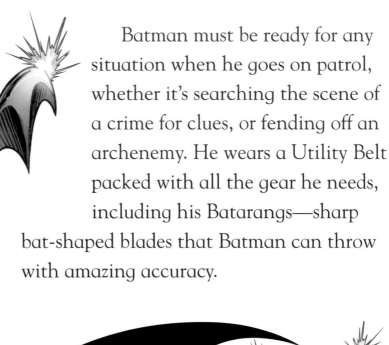

Batman must be ready for any situation when he goes on patrol, whether it's searching the scene of a crime for clues, or fending off an archenemy. He wears a Utility Belt packed with all the gear he needs, including his Batarangs—sharp bat-shaped blades that Batman can throw with amazing accuracy.

The Batarangs can be upgraded to emit sonic blasts or knockout gas—or can even explode! Batman also carries a grappling hook and rope for scaling walls, and lock picks for getting through locked doors.

Other important items in his Utility Belt include forensic tools such as a fingerprint kit for analyzing clues, surveillance equipment like cameras and listening devices, and titanium steel handcuffs to restrain the bad guys. Also, because villains like the Scarecrow and the Joker are often armed with toxic weapons or dangerous gases, Batman keeps plenty of medical supplies on hand to heal himself and others caught up in a conflict.

UTILITY BELT

Batman's Utility Belt enhances his abilities and improves his odds of winning a fight. Because he doesn't have superpowers, he must use cunning and technology to defeat villains. The Utility Belt has been a major part of Batman's arsenal, and its contents are always changing.

ADDITIONAL ITEMS

- A breathing mask, in case Batman is trapped at a location where air has been poisoned.

- A cutting tool, to slice through rope or anything that is being used to bind Batman.

- A fingerprint kit, ideal when he has to identify someone and he's not near the Batcave.

- Plastic explosives, which can blow up locked doors and walls.

- Toxins, powerful enough to knock out his strongest foes.

BATARANGS

These razor-sharp weapons are thrown with perfect precision by Batman.

COMMUNICATOR

A smart computerized device that can even make holographic recordings.

MINIATURE CAMERA

This digital camera also has a flash that can temporarily blind attackers!

GRAPPLING HOOK

Useful for scaling high walls and quick escapes

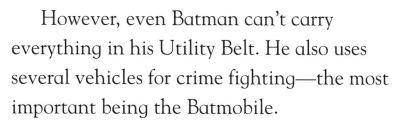

However, even Batman can't carry everything in his Utility Belt. He also uses several vehicles for crime fighting—the most important being the Batmobile.

Whenever the Bat-Signal shines above Gotham City, the Dark Knight races to the scene in his rocket-powered Batmobile. Like all of his equipment, the Batmobile has been modified several times over the years. It has evolved into a combination of high-speed performance racer, urban assault vehicle, and mobile crime-fighting lab.

The Batmobile is incredibly fast and maneuverable even though it is so heavily

shielded it can withstand armor-piercing
shells. It also carries additional medical
equipment, and its advanced on-board
computer system is linked to Batman's
powerful mainframe computer. This allows
Batman to control the Batmobile remotely,
meaning it can come to him wherever he
needs it. The Batmobile is also armed with
nonlethal offensive weapons, such as tear
gas emitters, smoke-screen grenades, tire-
piercing spikes, and super adhesive sprays.

BEYOND THE BATMOBILE

The Batmobile isn't the Dark Knight's only means of transportation. He has an amazing array of vehicles to get him on the scene—fast!

BATPLANE

The Batplane cost $46million (£30million) to build. When it reaches its cruising altitude of 35,000-45,0000ft (10,670-13,715m), its wings retract. Once it climbs above 55,000ft (16,765m), the Batplane enters stealth mode. Its "smart" paint reacts to the falling air pressure, camouflaging the plane's exterior.

BATCYCLE

When Batman needs a vehicle that is easier to move through crowded Gotham City streets than the Batmobile, he chooses the swift and maneuverable Batcycle. This mighty motorcycle is a modified street bike.

BAT-GLIDER

Not to be confused with the Batplane, this impressive device is designed to resemble a bat's wingspan and gives Batman the ability to fly. He hides various Bat-gliders around Gotham City.

BATBOAT

Batman's sleek watercraft is needed when he has to pursue criminals in Gotham City's river. The Batboat can reach up to 120mph (193kph) and can even travel underwater if required.

Locations

Its history is
centuries old, but
Gotham City truly took
shape when Alan Wayne,
Bruce Wayne's great-grandfather, funded its
transformation into a modern metropolis.

Already a thriving port, Gotham City
quickly grew into a mighty megacity—
thanks largely to the Wayne family's
enterprising spirit. But in the shadow of
progress and wealth, crime and corruption
soon spread through its streets.

Gotham City quickly became a breeding ground for mobsters, thieves and lowlifes. It also began to attract uncanny criminals such as the menacing metahuman Poison Ivy, and the Joker, a vile villain bent on creating malicious mayhem for a laugh.

Thankfully, Gotham City also has its share of heroes. Batman has inspired others, such as Commissioner Gordon, Robin, Batgirl, and even the good people of Gotham City to fight the growing evil that threatens their great city.

As heir to Wayne Enterprises, one of the world's largest multinational companies, Bruce Wayne pretends to be a billionaire playboy only interested in fast cars, parties, and spending money. That way no one suspects he is really Batman.

He makes his home at Wayne Manor, the grand estate where the Wayne family has lived for many generations. But like its owner, Wayne Manor harbors a secret—the Batcave! In the hidden caverns beneath the estate, Bruce has put his company's vast resources to good use. He has unrestricted access to all the computer electronics, chemical manufacturing, aeronautic equipment, robotics, and more to outfit his underground hideout with advanced technology and crime-fighting gear.

The Batcave contains a crime lab, engineering workshops, and a gym, as well as full medical facilities that can treat anything from broken bones to chemical exposure. However, Batman's greatest tool in his fight against crime is his Batcomputer, which allows him to keep an eye on everything happening in Gotham City, and gather information from around the world.

SECRETS OF THE BATCAVE

The Batcave contains a state-of-the-art crime lab, equipment workshops, a library, a gym, medical facilities, and the coolest garage in Gotham City!

1. TYRANNOSAURUS REX

Although he looks like he could go on the rampage at any moment, this mechanical Tyrannosaurus Rex is a trophy from Batman's adventure on Dinosaur Island. Batman likes a keepsake from every enemy he defeats!

2. VEHICLES

There is plenty of parking for the Batmobile, Batcycle, and even Bruce's Lamborghini sports car. The Batcave also has a hangar and dock.

3. LABS

The cave contains a fully-equipped crime lab as well as workshops to maintain Batman's amazing armor, weaponry, and vehicles. There is also a gym with up-to-the-minute training equipment to help the Dark Knight stay in peak condition.

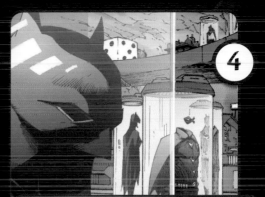

4. SECRET IDENTITY

The key to keeping Bruce Wayne's identity a secret is his Batsuit. The cave holds the various special suits he needs, as well as outfits for teammates, like Robin.

5. SECRET ENTRANCE

The Batcave can be reached using a variety of secret entrances. There are doors behind a clock and bookcase in Wayne Manor, a hidden passageway beneath Bruce Wayne's chair in Wayne Enterprises, and a tunnel for the Batmobile concealed by a hologram.

6. COMPUTERS

The Batcave boasts the latest technology so Batman can monitor crisis points anywhere. His satellite-linked Batcomputer gathers and stores all the data he requires to stay ahead of his enemies.

Arkham Asylum is a high-security psychiatric hospital on the edge of Gotham City. The hospital is home to some of the most notorious criminals that Batman has ever fought. Villains deemed to be too psychotic and violent for regular prisons like Blackgate are sent to Arkham. The Joker, the Riddler, and the Scarecrow have all been inmates at various times. Arkham also holds sane but dangerous villains who require special conditions to keep them under lock and key, such as the frosty Mr. Freeze and the toxic Poison Ivy. However, despite Arkham's many high-tech security measures, these crafty criminals often manage to escape.

Since it first opened, Arkham has badly affected many of the people connected to it. Amadeus Arkham, its founder, went insane and became a patient in his own hospital. His descendant, Jeremiah Arkham, was head psychiatrist until he became the villain Black Mask. The Joker's therapist became the crazy criminal Harley Quinn.

Arkham Asylum had to be rebuilt after the brutal warrior Bane led a large prison break by the inmates. The new institution is still as foreboding as the madmen it houses.

INSIDE THE MADHOUSE!

Over the years, many of Batman's most dangerous enemies have been imprisoned within Arkham Asylum's walls. Even the asylum's founder, Amadeus Arkham, was driven insane. Dare you venture inside?

Main catwalk to central tower

In a ploy to lure Batman into a trap, the Joker took over Arkham Asylum and freed several of its inmates, including Maxie Zeus and the Mad Hatter.

Heavy equipment outer doors

After Batman disappeared a few years ago and was presumed dead, Black Mask seized his chance and released the prisoners from Arkham Asylum, declaring himself their new leader.

A group of Batman's deadliest enemies, including Two-Face, the Scarecrow, and Killer Croc, once joined forces to break out of Arkham Asylum. Batman was forced to team up with the Joker to stop them.

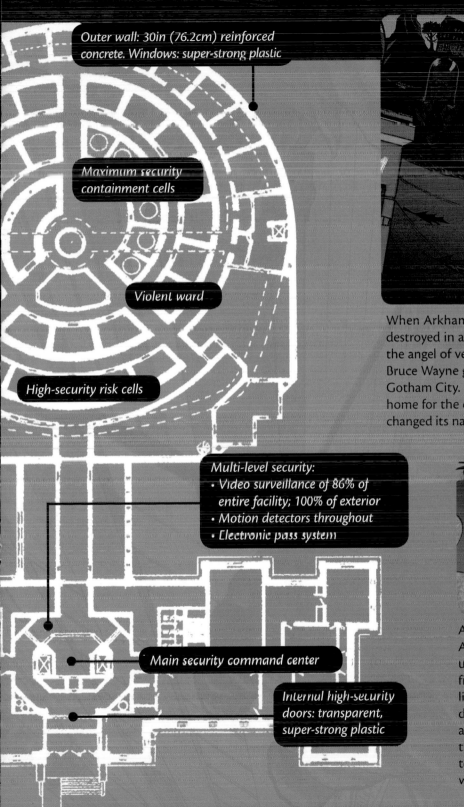

Outer wall: 30in (76.2cm) reinforced concrete. Windows: super-strong plastic

Maximum security containment cells

Violent ward

High-security risk cells

Multi-level security:
• Video surveillance of 86% of entire facility; 100% of exterior
• Motion detectors throughout
• Electronic pass system

Main security command center

Internal high-security doors: transparent, super-strong plastic

When Arkham Asylum was destroyed in an explosion caused by the angel of vengeance, The Spectre, Bruce Wayne gave Wayne Manor to Gotham City. It briefly became a home for the criminally insane and changed its name to Arkham Manor.

After a murder occurred at Arkham Manor, Batman went undercover as Jack Shaw to find the killer. Batman had to live among some of his deadliest foes like Mr. Freeze and Victor Zsasz to uncover the truth. The killer turned out to be a former laborer who went mad inside Arkham.

Fearsome foes

Batman has many enemies, but none compare to the Joker. This sinister clown is a comic genius at causing chaos in Gotham City. No one—not even Batman—is really sure of the Joker's true origin. Many think that he was once a member of the Red Hood Gang who fell into a vat of chemicals when he was chased by Batman through an old factory. The young man emerged from the blistering bath with his skin bleached white, his hair turned green, and his mind twisted beyond repair!

Despite his
madness, the
Joker exhibits
an amazing talent
for chemistry and
engineering.
He has created
an extremely
lethal arsenal of
acids, joy buzzers, and
novelty gags that no
one finds funny. "Joker venom"
is his most diabolical concoction.
Small doses can put people under his
control, while larger doses can make
them literally die laughing with
gruesome smiles on their faces.
Over the years, he has
masterminded many terrible plots
against his archenemy Batman. At
first, he only wanted to eliminate the Dark
Knight, but now he gets more sadistic glee
out of kidnapping and threatening those
closest to Batman, like Robin, Batgirl, and
other allies, with horrible deaths.

While treating the Joker at Arkham Asylum, Dr. Harleen Quinzel became hopelessly fascinated by the madman. When her own mind finally snapped, she took the name Harley Quinn and became the criminal clown's accomplice.

Harley Quinn is willing to go along with the Joker's schemes no matter how insane. However, she is more than just a sidekick. She is just as capable of cruelty as the Joker, and loves making mischief and mayhem of her own.

Harley Quinn is extremely acrobatic, and her madcap fighting style makes her a tricky opponent in hand-to-hand combat. She has successfully fought Batman and other heroes who can never be sure what move she is going to make next. Her current weapon of choice is an oversized mallet, but she's also very handy with her trusty pop gun.

She has been known to team up with Poison Ivy and Catwoman. However, like the Joker, Harley Quinn is too unstable to be trusted. Her alliances usually fall apart when she almost always veers away from the plan to follow her own wild impulses—often leaving her partners in the lurch!

District Attorney Harvey Dent was a beacon of light to the law-abiding citizens of Gotham City. For a time, he even became Batman's ally in his war on corruption in the city. Dent worked hard to put criminals behind bars, but despite his noble efforts, he was sometimes willing to go outside the law to get results. This darker side of his personality would one day overwhelm him when the mob horribly disfigured half of his face with acid and killed his wife.

Driven insane, Dent became Two-Face, a criminal with a split personality—rational one moment and monstrous the next. He came to believe that order or chaos should be decided with a toss of his scarred

coin: heads you live, tails you die! Over
the years, he has come into conflict with
Batman as he plotted to gain control
of Gotham City's underworld. He has
occasionally forged alarming alliances
with equally unpredictable villains like the
Joker and Scarecrow, only to be thwarted
by Batman or his own dual nature.

Batman continues to hope that he can
one day help Dent, but is the Dark Knight
merely a coin toss away from defeat?

Oswald Cobblepot was forever picked on as a boy because of his short stature and physical deformities, which gave him a birdlike appearance. The experience also gave him a fierce will to win and the ability to really hold a grudge. Nicknamed the Penguin, Cobblepot quickly proved himself to be smart and savage. By successfully working his way up in society through illegal activities, the Penguin became one of the leading figures in Gotham City's underworld. His actions eventually brought him into direct conflict with Batman, leading to many setbacks in his criminal fortunes.

Despite his dumpy demeanor, the Penguin is a very capable fighter, able to go

toe-to-toe with the Dark Knight. He also carries umbrellas armed with deadly surprises. Most models contain a razor-sharp sword hidden in the shaft that he can pull from the handle. Others release knockout gas to stun his foes, while another model is a camouflaged machine gun.

Opponents underestimate the Penguin at their own peril. He once made himself Mayor of Gotham City, and set the inmates of Arkham Asylum and Blackgate Prison against each other, until the Dark Knight removed him from office. Yet, try as he might, Batman can never keep this bad bird caged for long.

Much like the Penguin, Pamela Isley had a very troubled childhood. A rare, sensitive skin condition kept her at home, and having few friends to play with, she would spend her time in her family's shady garden, where her fascination with plant life took root. Years later, her knowledge of plant biology landed her a job at Wayne Enterprises in its bio-chemical division, but an accident with one of her experiments granted her the power to control plants and made her immune to all poisons, venoms, and even nasty viruses.

Taking the name Poison Ivy, she mostly enjoys being bad, though often in a very rash attempt to protect the environment. She once tricked the villain

Clayface into attacking the Penguin's
polluting factories, but her plan drew her
into direct combat against Batman.

On her good days, she has teamed up
with some of Batman's allies and even
helped the Dark Knight gain immunity to
the lethal Fear Toxin, created by the
sinister
Scarecrow.
With Ivy's
help,
Batman
was able
to save all of
Gotham City from
being poisoned.
However, no
matter what hint of
goodness may bloom
in her, Poison Ivy's
more wicked
ways always
sprout, causing
trouble to
grow.

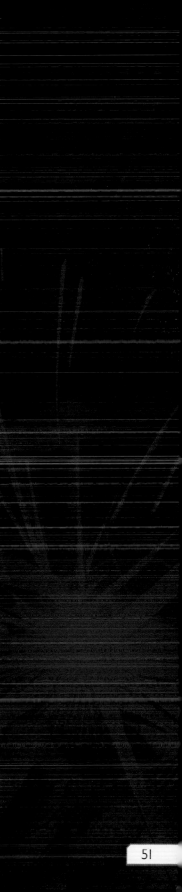

Having discovered the secret of near immortality, Rā's al Ghūl has mastered many fighting styles and acquired more skills and knowledge than anyone could learn in a single lifetime. As such, it makes him one of Batman's toughest opponents. More than six hundred years ago, Rā's discovered the fabled Lazarus Pits. By bathing in the Pits, his youth and vitality would be restored, and even deadly wounds could be healed.

He founded the League of Assassins to fight corruption, but by the 21st century, the League itself had become evil as Rā's slowly lost his sanity through continual use of the Lazarus Pits. Having fought the League and many of Rā's al Ghūl's allies, Batman eventually came face to face

with Rā's when the ageless fiend tried to
unleash a lethal virus on the world. They
have clashed several times since, with
Batman's intellect and tenacity always
defeating Rā's, and even earning him
the immortal's respect.

Despite their intense rivalry, their lives
became strangely entangled when Rā's al
Ghūl's daughter, Talia, gave birth to Batman's
son, Damian. The boy has often been caught
in the middle of his grandfather's intricate
and unending plots against his father!

Born in a brutal prison, Bane was raised in violence and quickly learned how to fight to survive. He grew into a man of immense size and muscle, who also showed savage intelligence, tactical genius, martial arts mastery, and, above all, iron-willed ambition. At some point during his life in prison, he was given a dangerous drug called Venom. It greatly enhanced his already prodigious strength, speed, and endurance to superhuman levels. With his newfound abilities, he finally escaped.

Bane headed to Gotham City, to take over the city's criminal gangs. As he made his plans, Bane studied Gotham City's protector, Batman, deducing that he was really Bruce Wayne. Bane ambushed Batman, breaking his back and leaving him for dead. However, Batman bounced back and eventually defeated Bane.

Over the years, Bane has proven to be one of the Dark Knight's deadliest adversaries. Unlike madmen such as the Joker, Bane and Batman acknowledge the noble qualities they share, like two brave fighters who know that a rematch is inevitable.

The secret society known as the Court of Owls has ruled Gotham City for hundreds of years. The members come from some of Gotham City's oldest and wealthiest families, who use power, money, and even murder to get their way.

Working silently from the shadows, their most terrifying weapons are their assassins known as the Talons. The Owls take young people, often circus performers who exhibit skills such as acrobatics and knife throwing, and train them to become ruthless enforcers of the court's judgments. They have even found a way to bring Talons back from the dead, making them seem frighteningly unstoppable! At one time, the Owls considered a young acrobat named Dick Grayson as a candidate for a Talon, but were thwarted when Bruce Wayne took the boy under his wing.

Their attempt to murder Bruce Wayne led them into open conflict with Batman and his allies. This led to the Owls being exposed, several of their Talons turning on them, and their organization falling into disarray. However, the Court of Owls is far from finished, and it continues to seek a verdict of death against the Dark Knight!

Deeply troubled by the tests of terror that his father put him through as a child, Jonathan Crane grew up wanting to control fear.

He slowly slid into a life of crime, becoming determined to spread dread and terror across Gotham City. He developed a Fear Toxin that could create horrifying hallucinations in his victims, and he wore a ragged mask and costume to become the Scarecrow.

Always able to conquer his fears, the Dark Knight has successfully defeated the Scarecrow many times. This gave the villain the ingenious idea of creating the vision of

a peaceful Gotham City in the minds of Batman and his allies to make them forget about fighting crime. For a while the plan worked, but the Dark Knight eventually saw through the delusion and brought the Scarecrow's dream of a Batman-free Gotham City to an end.

Despite this, Batman knows that the Scarecrow is always lurking in the shadows determined to give him a fatal fright!

Obsessed with riddles, wordplay, and intricate puzzles, young Edward Nygma grew up smugly thinking that he was smarter than most people around him. Clever and ambitious, he was eventually employed in an important position at Wayne Enterprises.

When Bruce Wayne returned from his travels to take over the company, a jealous Nygma hired the Red Hood Gang to kill Bruce. The plan failed, but it led Nygma to embrace a life of crime and take on a new persona as the Riddler.

His schemes grew ever more outlandish and at one point he was able to turn Gotham City into an overgrown jungle with a chemical developed by Poison Ivy. He set himself up as the king of this savage jungle, but in the survival of the fittest, he was no match for Batman. While imprisoned in Arkham Asylum, he proved to his fellow inmate, the Joker, that he was a master of strategy and escape, joining the insane clown in his latest fiendish escapade.

Although he's not nearly as psychotic as the Joker, Batman never underrates the Riddler, who always has a deadly question mark hanging over his head.

Basil Karlo wanted to be a famous actor, but he wasn't very talented. He agreed to work for the Penguin in exchange for a magic clay that the Penguin claimed could help his acting career. The substance entered his body, and Karlo developed the ability to alter his appearance—he could look like anyone he wanted. At first this helped him land better roles, but soon there were bad side effects that turned him into a violent, walking hunk of living clay.

Enjoying the criminal activities he performed for Penguin, Karlo embraced his new life as Clayface. He could imitate anyone, he

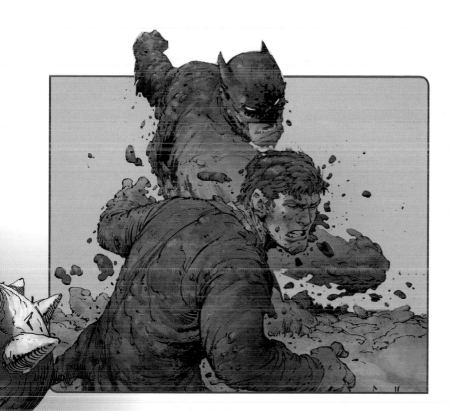

had great strength, and his flexible body
let him slip through tight spaces as well as
absorb punches and bullets. In the hopes of
getting rich quickly, he tried to impersonate
billionaire Bruce Wayne, not knowing he
was Batman. In the inevitable conflict,
the Dark Knight trapped Clayface in
a special container, but the villain was
able to slip through the hands of the
authorities. Now Batman can never
be sure whose face Clayface will
be wearing when they next meet.

Victor Fries had devoted his life to studying cryogenics and keeping things alive at sub-zero temperatures.

While working for Wayne Enterprises, Fries became obsessed with a cryogenically frozen woman named Nora. He fell in love with Nora and even began to believe that she was his wife. A lab accident doused Fries with experimental chemicals that turned him icy cold, forcing him to wear a special suit of armor that would allow him to survive in the normal temperature of the outside world.

Building a freeze gun, Fries set out on a criminal spree across Gotham City as Mr. Freeze. He wanted to steal enough money to enable

him to continue his research and reclaim
Nora, with the desperate hope of one day
being able to revive her.

In addition to his own highly warped
scientific schemes, he has teamed up with
Batman's enemies on several occasions.
However, no matter what his plans, this
ice-cold criminal always gets put back
in deep freeze by the Dark Knight.

Waylon Jones was born with a horrific genetic mutation that made him look like a large human crocodile. He has tough, scaly skin that can deflect bullets and hard blows. His sharp claws can tear through wood and concrete just as easily as they can his opponents. He is savagely strong and fast, despite his huge size. This has all earned him the feared name Killer Croc.

Bullied his whole life because of his strange looks, he became a ferocious fighter and a criminal to survive. He also protects the homeless and the helpless who are forced to live in the sewers below Gotham City. He has sided with villains such as Scarecrow against Batman, but mostly to defend his subterranean kingdom of outcasts. He once was beaten by the mighty Bane in combat, and has acted as a bodyguard for Selina Kyle, aka Catwoman. Still, Batman knows that the cold-blooded killer in Croc is waiting to surface and will one day snap!

Dr. Kirk Langstrom was searching for a way to help deaf and blind children, but the formula that he discovered had unforeseen and hideous side effects. Langstrom developed the features of a bat. He grew fur, sharp claws, and fangs. He could fly with leathery wings, and his long ears gave him the power of echolocation: He could use sound to "see" in the dark.

He had become the Man-Bat! At first, Langstrom was Batman's ally, but later the Dark Knight suspected that his Man-Bat side was growing much wilder. He worried that Man-Bat had committed a series of gruesome murders that he couldn't remember. Langstrom soon realized that his wife Francine had also used a

version of the formula on herself—one that contained the DNA of a vampire bat. He had not committed the murders; she had! Not only that, she liked being a bat creature, and even called herself the Bat-Queen.

Man-Bat would eventually turn bad and team up with the Dark Knight's enemies, but Batman still hopes that he can find a cure for this scientist-turned-monster.

BATMAN'S GREATEST BATTLES!

Batman has been protecting Gotham City for years, but some villains just don't know when to quit. Here are some of the Dark Knight's toughest fights.

During one battle, **Bane** enhanced his strength with a new version of the drug, Venom. Just as Bane was about to hurl Batman over a cliff, the Dark Knight made his foe swallow a Venom antidote. With Bane in a weakened state, Batman managed to push him into the sea.

The **Joker** is one of the few villains who has come close to defeating Batman. He once took advantage of an impaired Batman to release a poison into the air that turned its victims into copies of the Joker. Batman was even imprisoned in Arkham Asylum and, once freed, he was forced to turn to the evil Court of Owls for help in bringing down the Joker.

Rā's al Ghūl, one of Batman's greatest foes, has tried to kill him on countless occasions. When the Dark Knight first encountered the powerful villain, Ghūl challenged him to a spectacular sword fight, which Batman ultimately won.

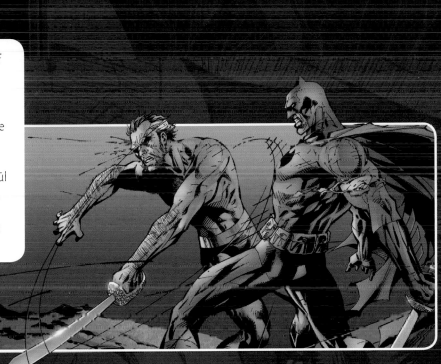

The **Scarecrow** has clashed with the Dark Knight many times. On one occasion, he managed to kidnap Batman and infect him with a Fear Toxin. With Superman's help, Batman fought off the toxin's effects and he subdued the Scarecrow.

The Court of Owls' assassins, the **Talons**, once captured Batman and placed him in their malicious maze. The Talons tried everything to break the Dark Knight's spirit, but when he saw a picture of Alan Wayne, an ancestor killed by the Talons, he found the strength to win.

The **Riddler** took over Gotham City for a whole year, forcing Bruce Wayne to go underground. The Riddler was stopped thanks to Batman's cunning and help from some of his closest allies, including James Gordon—a police sergeant at the time.

Awesome allies

Batman has many allies in his war against crime and evil. None is more trusted than Alfred Pennyworth. Alfred has been the butler at Wayne Manor for many years, and raised Bruce after his parents were murdered.

Alfred's duties run far beyond those of any normal butler. In addition to making sure that everything at Wayne Manor runs smoothly, he helps Bruce Wayne keep up his image as a billionaire playboy. He also maintains Batman's suits, the Batmobile, and all the workings of the Batcave, in readiness for the Dark Knight's next mission.

Having served in the military, he has fighting and medical experience as well. From the

Batcomputer, Alfred is able to provide valuable information to Batman while he is out on patrol. He also attends to Batman's wounds in the Batcave's high-tech medical facility.

Even though Alfred is often critical of the serious risks taken by Batman, he is fiercely loyal and dependable. He has also helped several of Batman's friends, especially his young protégés, like Robin.

Robin fights alongside Batman, and several people have assumed that vital role over the years, becoming heroes in their own right. Batman has taken these young apprentices under his wing to train them and help them focus their talent and energy into helping him rid Gotham City of crime.

No Robin is dearer to Batman than Damian Wayne, his son. His mother is Talia al Ghūl, the daughter of Rā's al Ghūl—one of the world's greatest villains! Despite this, after Damian met his father, he chose to fight on the side of good. Fatally wounded in a vicious battle with The Heretic, Damian was restored to life by Batman using alien technology. As father and son, they share an unbreakable bond in their quest for justice.

THE MANY FACES OF
ROBIN

Batman often works with a younger ally, Robin, to keep the streets of Gotham City safe. There have been four boys who have adopted this role. The first was Dick Grayson, followed by Jason Todd and Tim Drake. The newest Robin is Bruce Wayne's own son, Damian.

JASON TODD
Batman first met Jason Todd when the street criminal tried to steal the Batmobile's tires. Batman placed him in a school for youngsters in trouble with the law, before making him the second Robin. Jason now fights crime as the Red Hood and is prepared to use lethal force.

DICK GRAYSON
Orphaned when his acrobat parents were killed, Dick Grayson was adopted by Bruce Wayne who taught him to use his skills to combat crime. Many years later he became the costumed hero Nightwing, and now operates undercover as Agent 37.

TIM DRAKE

After watching Dick Grayson in action at the circus, Tim Drake worked out the secret identities of Batman and Robin. He followed their adventures and when the two super heroes were captured, he became Robin to rescue them! He has also changed his crime-fighting identity, and now battles evil as the Red Robin.

DAMIAN WAYNE

The latest Robin is the son of Bruce Wayne and Talia al Ghūl, the daughter of one of Batman's most dangerous foes, Rā's al Ghūl. Damian died during a fierce fight, but was brought back to life soon afterwards, with short-lived superpowers.

Super heroes aren't the only people in Gotham City fighting crime. James Gordon is the commissioner of the Gotham City Police Department (G.C.P.D.) and Batman's ally. Gordon shines the Bat-Signal in the sky to let Batman know he's needed.

Many people question why their police commissioner works with a vigilante. However, Gordon knows what might happen if Batman was not around to protect the city against the likes of the Joker, the Scarecrow, and even the police force itself!

The Gotham City Police Department has been troubled by corruption for many years. G.C.P.D. members, from uniformed officers to high-ranking officials, have been linked to criminal activity. However, there are still some honest cops on the force, like the gruff Harvey Bullock, and his whip-smart partner, Renee Montoya. Both back Commissioner Gordon's association

with Batman. Yet they all fear that if the Dark Knight steps too far outside the law, they'll have no choice but to bring him to justice.

Selina Kyle is the orphaned daughter of a Gotham City crime boss. At an early age she became a thief and cat burglar—talents that she excelled at. Selina later adopted the identity of Catwoman, and her successful criminal career brought her to the attention of Batman.

Armed with sharp claws on her gloves and a whip that she wields with great skill, Catwoman is an impressive opponent. While not superhuman, her agility, speed, reflexes, and stealth border on being genuinely feline. Her abilities as a thief to scale walls, slip into small spaces, and get past any form of security are second to none. Added to that, she has been trained in multiple forms of hand-to-hand combat, making her an accomplished and fearsome fighter. She has fought Batman on several occasions and has often come out on top.

Over time, Catwoman has changed her criminal ways, and she now fights on the side of good—though it is always on her own terms. She and Batman have become allies and even share romantic feelings for each other. However, their crusade to make Gotham City a safer place for its citizens always comes first.

Batman has had several young allies who have worn the Robin costume, before his son, Damian, took on the role. Tim Drake was a superb detective. Jason Todd's dark personality made him the most driven. However, the very first Robin was Dick Grayson.

Dick grew up as a circus acrobat, but a mobster killed his parents, leaving him an orphan. Bruce Wayne took the boy into his care and revealed to him that he was Batman. Building on Dick's acrobatic abilities, Bruce trained him to be a fellow crusader, helping him become adept at using weapons such as batons and staffs.

When he was older, Dick parted ways with Batman and set out on his own, becoming the hero Nightwing. Occasionally, he has returned to help his mentor— sometimes even becoming Batman when Bruce

Wayne was injured—and has come to the aid of other members of the crime-fighting Batman family. At Batman's request, Dick has gone undercover to infiltrate the mysterious criminal organization called Spyral, where he is known as Agent 37.

Commissioner Gordon's daughter, Barbara, grew up wanting to be a super hero. Incredibly smart and athletic, she came to the attention of Batman. Barbara trained with the Dark Knight and was soon fighting alongside him and Robin as Batgirl. Tragedy struck when she was shot and paralyzed by the Joker, ending her crime-fighting career for a short time.

With a combination of rigorous training, innovative surgery,

and steely determination she fully recovered and returned to battle crime. Her many talents include a genius intellect, a flawless memory and a mastery of many forms of martial arts, including judo and kickboxing. She is also great at wielding a baton, and can throw Batarangs with pinpoint precision. Best of all, Batgirl is a highly skilled computer engineer and hacker—even more so than Batman! She once created a computer virus to wipe clean the information from a villain's mind. She has also lent her extensive skills to the all-female super hero team, the Birds of Prey, helping them to clean up Gotham City.

ARE YOU READY TO JOIN THE BATMAN FAMILY?

The Dark Knight often teams up with other heroes to keep Gotham City safe. Take this quiz to find out which ally's talents you share the most—and learn about other members of the Batman family.

1. You're about to patrol the streets of Gotham City. What's the most important thing you'll need?

a. Dark clothes, so you're not seen by any villains ⋯⋯ ★

b. As much technology as your Utility Belt can carry ⋯⋯ 🌢

c. A couple of flares to help get you out of a tough spot ⋯⋯ ◆

d. Just your skill and instincts ⋯⋯ ♥

2. You've spotted a possible crime taking place. What do you do first?

a. Take out your radar scanner and check how many villains are up ahead ⋯⋯ 🌢

b. Sneak a bit closer to assess the situation ⋯⋯ ★

c. Leap straight into the action—you can handle it ⋯⋯ ♥

d. Create a diversion to distract most of the bad guys ⋯⋯ ◆

3. Batman has asked you along on a mission. How do you help out?

a. Fight right alongside him. Wherever he goes, you go ⋯⋯ ♥

b. Rescue him the moment it looks like he's about to be defeated ⋯⋯ ◆

c. Check out the area before Batman arrives to find all potential threats ⋯⋯ ★

d. Update his Utility Belt, so that he has the most suitable gear ⋯⋯ 🌢

4. Which villain would be the easiest to beat?
a. Bane—he might have strength, but you have skill ...... ♥

b. Poison Ivy—you could talk her into teaming up rather than fighting ...... ★

c. The Riddler—you'd use your weapons to surprise him while he's mid-riddle ...... ◆

d. Rā's al Ghūl—you'd confuse this ancient villain with your new technology ...... ◗

5. Which color do you wear most?
a. Blue ◗   b. Red ★   c. Silver ♥   d. Orange ◆

BATWOMAN
Highly skilled in hand-to-hand combat, Batwoman's greatest talent is her stealth. Trained by her ex-military father, her secret identity is Kate Kane, and she has become a real force to be reckoned with.

BATWING
Batwing is Luke Fox, the son of Bruce Wayne's friend and boss of Wayne Enterprises, Lucius Fox. Luke is great at martial arts and uses a special Batsuit so he can fly over Gotham City on the lookout for crime.

BLUEBIRD
Bluebird, aka Harper Row, grew up in the Narrows of Gotham City with her younger brother. Bluebird is a genius with electronics and, after a tough upbringing, she can deal with any situation that is thrown at her.

HAWKFIRE
Hawkfire is Batwoman's cousin, Bette Kane. She is a superb gymnast and kickboxer, and is kitted out with retractable wings, flares, and a wrist-mounted flamethrower—some villains find her too hot to handle!

The Justice League is a group of super heroes who band together to defend Earth from dangers greater than any one of them could face alone. The team began when Batman partnered with the power ring–wearing Green Lantern to fight the demonic Darkseid. Knowing that Superman was the mightiest being on the planet, they enlisted his help and the Justice League was born.

Soon, other heroes joined, including the Amazon warrior, Wonder Woman; The Fastest Man Alive, The Flash; the half-man, half-machine, Cyborg; and ruler of the underwater kingdom of Atlantis, Aquaman.

Together, they have overcome conquerors from Earth and outer space. They have also faced more sinister threats like the Amazo Virus, created by the villainous Lex Luthor, which gave super powers to ordinary people, turning them evil! When Batman was infected by the virus, the Justice League teamed up with Luthor to save mankind… and their friend.

THE JUSTICE LEAGUE

With so many powerful villains, the world can be a very dangerous place. Luckily, Batman has the Justice League as allies, whom he can call on for help.

SUPERMAN

Born on the doomed planet, Krypton, Superman was sent to Earth as a baby. His real name is Kal-El, but the humans who adopted him named him Clark Kent.

POWERS: Flying, super-strength, super-speed, heat vision, and breath that can freeze anything.

WONDER WOMAN

Born on Paradise Island, also called Themiscyra, Wonder Woman is an Amazonian princess. She is the daughter of Queen Hippolyta and Zeus, king of the Greek gods.

POWERS: Super-strength, flying, indestructible bracelets, and the Lasso of Truth, which forces others to reveal their secrets.

THE FLASH

Barry Allen is a police scientist whose life was changed forever when a lightning bolt struck his lab, causing chemicals to spill over him.

POWERS: Super-speed, healing, and passing through objects.

CYBORG

Victor Stone was attacked by a creature from an inter-dimensional portal. The only way he could survive was for his father, Silas, to create a cyborg body for him.

POWERS: Super-strength, genius-level intellect, and flying.

GREEN LANTERN

Hal Jordan was a fighter pilot when he met Abin Sur, a dying alien who was part of an intergalactic police force. Hal's fearlessness made him the obvious choice to replace Sur.

POWERS: Uses his power ring to fly and make real whatever he can imagine.

AQUAMAN

Arthur Curry is the son of lighthouse keeper Tom Curry and Atlanna, who came from the underwater kingdom of Atlantis. He gave up the throne of Atlantis to become a super hero.

POWERS: The ability to swim super-fast, enhanced strength, and mind control over sea creatures.

Quiz

1. What terrible incident makes Bruce Wayne determined to fight crime?

2. Who were Bruce Wayne's teachers as he traveled around the world learning how to improve himself?

3. Which criminal does Batman disguise himself as when he goes undercover to get information?

4. Who is Batman's greatest foe?

5. How much can Batman lift?

6. Who is the latest Robin?

7. Batman's bulletproof suit is made out of which materials?

8. What giant mechanical creature is kept in the Batcave as a trophy?

9. How much did the Batplane cost to build?

10. What is Harley Quinn's current weapon of choice?

11. Which feathered court works outside the law to bring down Batman?

12. How does the G.C.P.D.'s Commissioner Gordon contact Batman?

13. Which criminal organization has Dick Grayson infiltrated as Agent 37?

14. What is Batwoman's relationship to Hawkfire?

15. Which all-powerful alien villain first brought the Justice League together to fight him?

See page 94 for answers.

Glossary

Acrobatic
The ability to perform gymnastic feats with great skill.

Arsenal
A collection of weapons.

Assassin
Someone hired to kill.

Camouflage
Hiding something using a disguise.

Concoction
A mixture of different things.

Contingency
An alternate or emergency plan.

DNA
A substance that carries the genetic information of plants and animals.

Demeanor
A person's appearance and behavior.

Eco-terrorist
Someone who uses extreme measures to stop damage to the environment.

Echolocation
Using sound and echoes to get around in the dark.

Engulf
To flow over and enclose something.

Foreboding
A feeling something bad will happen.

Forensic
Using scientific methods to solve crime.

Formidable
Possessing immense power or ability.

Genetic / Genes
Part of a cell that controls the growth and appearance of living things.

Hacker
A person who secretly gains access to a computer system to get at someone else's data.

Hallucinations
Something experienced only in the mind that seems real but is not.

Hologram
A three-dimensional image produced by light.

Immortality
The ability to live forever.

Impaired
Reduced or weakened in strength.

Infiltrate
To join a group to secretly obtain information from them.

Innovative
Using new methods or ideas.

Inter-dimensional
An imagined dimension or place beyond our own.

Intergalactic
The vast space between galaxies.

Kevlar
Strong, lightweight material used to make items bulletproof.

Lethal
Very dangerous and may cause death.

Quiz answers
1. The murder of his parents.
2. Shihan Matsuda and Sergei Alexandrov 3. Matches Malone
4. The Joker 5. 1,000lb
6. Damian Wayne 7. Titanium and Kevlar 8. Tyrannosaurus Rex
9. £30million ($46million)
10. An oversized mallet
11. The Court of Owls
12. He lights up the Bat-Signal
13. Spyral 14. She is her cousin.
15. Darkseid

Malicious
Intending to do harm to someone.

Martial arts
A traditional Asian form of fighting
or self-defense, like karate and judo.

Mentor
A trusted and experienced teacher.

Metahuman
Someone with superhuman powers.

Mutation
A genetic change in a plant or animal.

Notorious
Someone or something famous for
being bad.

Outlandish
Something that is wild and unusual.

Persona
A person's outward personality.

Psychotic
A mad, insane person.

Prodigious
Something that is amazing,
marvelous, or very big.

Protégé
A young person who is taught by
someone with a lot of experience.

Regime
A regular activity.

Rehabilitate
Restore someone's good health
or reputation.

Retractable
To pull something back into
something that encloses it.

Subterranean
Located or living underground

Stake out / Surveillance
Carefully watching someone,
to prevent a crime.

Thermal
The ability of special garments to
retain heat.

Toxic
Containing poisonous material.

Titanium
A very strong and flexible metal.

Vigilante
Someone who fights crime outside
of the law.

BATMAN™

CHARACTER PROFILES

WRITTEN BY **MATTHEW K. MANNING**

BATMAN

VITAL STATS

Real Name: Bruce Wayne

Occupation: Hero, crime fighter

Height: 6ft 2in

Weight: 210 lbs

Base: Gotham City

Allies: The Batman Family, the Justice League, Batman, Inc.

Foes: Arkham Rogues, Rā's al Ghūl, the Penguin

POWERS AND ABILITIES

Martial artist; near-genius intellect; skilled detective and gymnast; armored suit and Utility Belt equipped with myriad offensive and defensive devices.

BEWARE THE BAT

Bruce Wayne adopted the image of a bat in order to strike fear into the hearts of criminals everywhere. This intimidating persona was inspired by Bruce's own childhood encounter with the bats living below Wayne Manor.

After his parents were gunned down before his eyes in a senseless act of violence when he was just a young boy, Bruce Wayne dedicated his entire life to protecting the citizens of Gotham City. To that end, he trained his body and mind to near physical perfection and used the Wayne family fortune to create a hi-tech arsenal of unique weapons and vehicles.

"Father, I shall become a bat."

Arm gauntlets adorned with scallops that can be used as weapons

Cape helps instill fear in criminals and protects him from gunfire and flames

Bat-symbol has helped make him notorious

Armored Batsuit has reinforced plates at the knees

BRUCE WAYNE

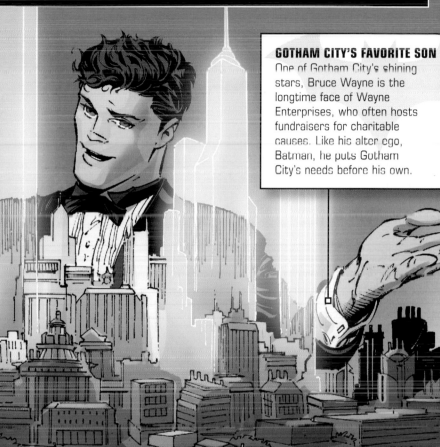

VITAL STATS

Full Name: Bruce Wayne

Occupation: Former head of Wayne Enterprises

Height: 6ft 2in

Weight: 210 lbs

Base: Gotham City

Allies: The Batman Family, the Justice League, Batman, Inc.

Foes: Arkham Rogues, Ra's al Ghul, the Penguin

POWERS AND ABILITIES

Near-genius intellect; incredible social skills; carefully constructed public persona conceals alter ego; enormous resources at his disposal due to contacts at Wayne Enterprises.

GOTHAM CITY'S FAVORITE SON

One of Gotham City's shining stars, Bruce Wayne is the longtime face of Wayne Enterprises, who often hosts fundraisers for charitable causes. Like his alter ego, Batman, he puts Gotham City's needs before his own.

Bruce Wayne became the Batman, fighting to protect Gotham City. However, when he returned to his hometown from traveling and training abroad, he realized the need to create a public persona that would distance him from his nocturnal activities. Bruce became involved in Wayne Enterprises, and built a reputation for himself as a careless bachelor.

"A better, brighter Gotham is just one dream away."

Hides in plain sight as public figure

Often dresses formally for social engagements

Can change into Batsuit at lightning speed

Tuxedo from his expensive wardrobe

ROBIN

VITAL STATS

Real Name: Damian Wayne

Occupation: Hero, adventurer

Height: 4ft 6in

Weight: 84 lbs

Base: Gotham City

Allies: Batman, the Batman Family, Batman, Inc., Goliath

Foes: Rās al Ghūl, the League of Assassins, NoBody

POWERS AND ABILITIES

Martial artist; skilled detective and gymnast; adept assassin; impressive intellect; as Robin, employs armored suit equipped with a myriad of offensive and defensive devices; protected by a Man-Bat named Goliath; briefly possessed Superman-like powers.

FATHER AND SON

Batman has mentored several Robins, but none have been his own flesh and blood until Damian. Despite his stubborn personality, Damian holds a special place in the Dark Knight's carefully guarded heart.

The result of a romance between Batman and the corrupt Talia al Ghūl, Damian Wayne was grown in a lab. Once he was brought into the world, Talia trained Damian in the deadly ways of the League of Assassins before allowing Batman to meet his son. Damian soon abandoned his mother's violent ways and joined his father as his new partner, Robin.

"I'm going out, Father. Gotham needs me."

Trained in martial arts

Utility Belt with smoke pellets and tear gas

Gauntlets similar to Batman's

VITAL STATS

Full Name: Richard "Dick" Grayson

Occupation: Agent of Spyral, gymnastics teacher

Height: 5ft 10in

Weight: 175 lbs

Base: Saint Hadrian's Finishing School for Girls, England

Allies: Batman, the Batman Family, Helena Bertinelli, Starfire

Foes: The Joker, Prankster, Paragon, Tony Zucco

POWERS AND ABILITIES

Highly skilled acrobat; natural athlete; martial artist; extremely intelligent; trained by Batman; can alter appearance via identity protection implants.

LIGHTS OUT AT MIDNIGHT

Grayson's adventures with Spyral have put him in direct opposition with the vigilante known as the Midnighter on several occasions. What Midnighter doesn't know is that Grayson is secretly a double agent for Batman.

Equipped with mind-influencing "hypnos"

Favorite weapons are escrima sticks

Belt equipped with variety of hi-tech gadgets

Soon after young trapeze artist Dick Grayson watched his parents fall to their deaths, he embarked on a new chapter in his life as Bruce Wayne's adopted son and Batman's partner, Robin. After growing into a Super Hero in his own right, Nightwing, Dick later retired that name after a near-death experience, and went to work at the spy agency Spyral as Agent 37.

"We've got some lives to save."

BATGIRL

VITAL STATS

Real Name: Barbara Gordon
Occupation: Hero, graduate student
Height: 5ft 11in
Weight: 135 lbs
Base: Burnside, Gotham City
Allies: The Birds of Prey, the Batman Family, James Gordon
Foes: The Joker, James Gordon, Jr., Knightfall, Velvet Tiger

POWERS AND ABILITIES

Expert martial artist and gymnast; intelligent and excellent strategist; natural leader; athletic and agile; uses compactible Batcycle; trained by Batman.

PACKING A PUNCH

Batgirl has worn several costumes over the years. She adopted her second official uniform when returning to crime fighting after a temporary hiatus. This costume was highly armored and utilized all of Batman's technology.

Can remember with expert precision

Designed her own protective costume

Smartphone to use social media to her advantage

Fully stocked Utility Belt

The daughter of police commissioner James Gordon, Barbara Gordon idolized Batman from a young age. One day, at police headquarters, Barbara adopted a police-developed Batsuit to protect her brother from an escaping criminal. After Batman complimented her on her actions, she realized her true calling and donned a mask and cape as Batgirl.

"Shut up and hug, tough girl."

BATWOMAN

VITAL STATS

Real Name: Katherine (Kate) Kane

Occupation: Hero, socialite

Height: 5ft 11in

Weight: 141 lbs

Base: Gotham City

Allies: Hawkfire, Batman, the Batman Family, the Unknowns

Foes: Nocturna, Ceto, Wolf Spider, Mr. Bones

POWERS AND ABILITIES

Martial artist; skilled detective and gymnast; highly trained soldier; studied under elite operatives known as the Murder of Crows.

ESTRANGED FAMILY

Unlike Batgirl or Robin, Batwoman doesn't operate with Batman's seal of approval. The two clashed when Batwoman's then employers, the Department of Extranormal Operations (D.E.O.), ordered her to find out the Dark Knight's secret identity.

Bruce Wayne's cousin Kate Kane lived a happy life, until her mother was killed. Kate was raised by her father, Colonel Jacob Kane, whose military connections enabled her to train with some of the world's finest fighters. Kate struggled to find her direction in life until an encounter with Batman inspired her to fight crime in her own unique style as Batwoman.

"I will soldier on."

Wears long-haired wig to mask identity

Arm gauntlets can fire grappling line

Protective suit equipped with myriad devices

Utility Belt houses array of useful tools

ALFRED PENNYWORTH

VITAL STATS

Full Name: Alfred Pennyworth
Occupation: Bruce Wayne's butler
Height: 6ft
Weight: 160 lbs
Base: Gotham City
Allies: Batman, the Batman Family, Julia Pennyworth
Foes: Arkham Rogues, Hush

POWERS AND ABILITIES

Skilled surgeon; military combat training; expert actor; computer expert; valued confidant.

A STEADY HAND

There is far more to Alfred's responsibilities than cooking and cleaning for billionaire Bruce Wayne. With full knowledge of Batman's identity, Alfred has saved Bruce's life on many occasions, putting his surgery skills to good use.

As loyal butler to Thomas and Martha Wayne, Alfred Pennyworth did his best to raise their son Bruce after their tragic deaths. Alfred stood by his young master's side, helping him build his career as Batman. While he often wishes Bruce would retire from crime fighting, Alfred nevertheless feels honored to play a role in Batman's mission.

"...I'll always be there to patch you up."

Dubbed Penny-One during radio transmissions, Alfred often works at the Batcomputer, feeding Batman information when he is in the field.

JULIA PENNYWORTH

VITAL STATS

Full Name: Julia Pennyworth

Occupation: Batman task force strategist, former SRR agent

Height: 5ft 8in

Weight: 129 lbs

Base: Gotham City

Allies: Batman, James Gordon, Alfred Pennyworth, G.C.P.D.

Foes: Shen Fang, Hush, the Joker

POWERS AND ABILITIES

Highly trained special agent; expert marksman; computer expert; efficient spy and strategist; has access to Batman's crime files and technology.

IN FOR A PENNY...

Julia began helping Batman from the Batcave as Penny-Two after Alfred was injured by Hush. After Batman's assumed "death," she began working as part of the G.C.P.D.'s Batman task force as Julia Perry.

An agent for the British Special Reconnaissance Regiment, Julia Pennyworth first crossed paths with Batman in Hong Kong when he was investigating Carmine Falcone and Shen Fang. Fang stabbed Julia, badly injuring her. Learning that Julia was Alfred's daughter, Batman brought her to Wayne Manor, where she discovered his double life and reconciled with her father, Alfred.

"Turn on the lights down here and show Jim his Batmobile."

It didn't take Julia long to figure out the Batcomputer. She usually assists from the Batcave, but has occasionally ventured out into the field.

BLUEBIRD

VITAL STATS

Real Name: Harper Row

Occupation: Hero, student

Height: 5ft 5in

Weight: 112 lbs

Base: Gotham City

Allies: Batman, Red Robin, the Batman Family, Cullen Row

Foes: The Mad Hatter, the Joker, Lincoln March

POWERS AND ABILITIES

Electronics expert; great at fixing things; protective suit equipped with myriad offensive and defensive devices; uses taser rifle.

NO KILLING A MOCKINGBIRD

After repeatedly proving her worth to Batman, Harper Row began to fight by Red Robin's side. She eventually developed her own identity as Bluebird to battle the Mad Hatter, and became Batman's newest ally.

The daughter of a deadbeat father, Harper Row was forced to take on responsibilities at an early age and practically raised her brother Cullen. As a teenager with a talent for electronics, she and her brother were rescued by the Batman one night. Inspired by the hero, Harper hacked into his network and helped in a battle with Tiger Shark.

"Batman doesn't get to die."

Cut hair to take a stand against brother's bullies

Suit has anti-nanotechnology barrier

Belt contains smoke capsules and Batarangs

HAWKFIRE

VITAL STATS

Real Name: Bette Kane

Occupation: Student, crime fighter

Height: 5ft 6in

Weight: 120 lbs

Base: Gotham City

Allies: Batwoman, Jacob Kane

Foes: The Hook, Mr. Freeze, Bane

POWERS AND ABILITIES

Martial artist; skilled detective and gymnast; trained by Batwoman and Jacob Kane; studied under elite operatives known as the Murder of Crows; wing pack allows her to fly.

A DYNAMIC DUO?

Hawkfire is the optimistic Robin to Batwoman's more practical Batman. Full of life and hope, with more than a little skill of her own, Hawkfire has proven herself as a true crime fighter, despite Batwoman's concerns.

Bette Kane's desire to be a Super Hero was long held. Originally operating as the crime-fighting heroine Flamebird, Bette learned that her cousin Kate Kane was moonlighting as Batwoman. Kate took her cousin under her wing and Bette adopted the identity of Hawkfire. Operating as Batwoman's sometime partner, Bette is helped out by her uncle, Jacob Kane.

> **"You don't know how badly I need this..."**

Lenses in mask similar to Batwoman's

Gauntlets equipped with flamethrowers

Costume possibly inspired by Nightwing's

Protective suit fitted with functioning wings

CATWOMAN

VITAL STATS

Real Name: Selina Kyle
Occupation: Crime boss and thief, sometime hero, owner of Egyptian Casino
Height: 5ft 7in
Weight: 128 lbs
Base: Gotham City
Allies: Killer Croc, the Justice League of America, Batman, Inc., Alice Tesla
Foes: The Joker's Daughter, Bone, Black Mask

POWERS AND ABILITIES

Master cat burglar; expert fighter; accomplished gymnast. Weapons include cat-o-nine-tails whip and gloves with diamond-tipped claws.

GIVING BACK

Selina Kyle learned to steal at an early age while living at an orphanage. She became an expert cat burglar, but retains a strict moral code that compels her to protect the underprivileged, often joining forces with Batman.

Selina Kyle's father is the notorious former Gotham City crime boss, Rex "the Lion" Calabrese. She unknowingly began to follow in his footsteps after being thrown from a rooftop when investigating her own past. She crafted a Catwoman costume out of the awning that saved her life, later rising up the ranks of the underworld to become a crime boss herself.

"In case you hadn't noticed, I don't fight crime, I am crime."

Many gadgets devised by Alice Tesla

Belt doubles as a whip

Bodysuit allows freedom of movement

BATWING

VITAL STATS

Real Name: Lucas "Luke" Fox

Occupation: Hero, mixed martial arts fighter

Height: 5ft 9in

Weight: 170 lbs

Base: Gotham City

Allies: Batman, Lucius Fox, the Batman Family, Batman, Inc.

Foes: Lady Vic, Ratcatcher, Charlie Caligula, Menace

POWERS AND ABILITIES

Talented martial arts fighter; brilliant designer and engineer; quick witted; suit allows for hi-tech weaponry and defense systems, flight and limited invisibility; near unlimited access to Wayne Enterprises technology.

WINGING IT

One of Batwing's first missions had him partner with Batman to face the Marabunta, an ant-like colony of villains employed by the criminal Charlie Caligula. Batwing defeated the organization's sects in Africa and Gotham City.

When Batman formed his crime-fighting organization, Batman, Inc., he hand-picked worthy individuals to join the team. He chose Luke, son of his longtime friend—and Wayne Enterprises CEO—Lucius Fox, to become the armored hero Batwing. While his secret Batwing career has caused family problems for Luke, he has embraced life as a Super Hero.

"It's all part of my job."

Bat-symbol can project bursts of brilliant light

Helmet equipped with "Detective Vision"

Built-in Utility Belt to store small devices

Bulletproof armor protects and seals underwater

Gauntlets can fire grappling line

THE BIRDS OF PREY

VITAL STATS

Team Name: The Birds of Prey
Base: Gotham City
Allies: Batman, the Batman Family, Mother Eve
Foes: The Penguin, Mr. Freeze, Rā's al Ghūl

Members: Batgirl, Black Canary, Katana, Strix, Condor, Poison Ivy (traitor), Starling (traitor)

ENEMIES AND FRENEMIES

The Birds of Prey fought several villains including Mr. Freeze, Rā's al Ghūl, and even former teammate, Poison Ivy. Team members often had trouble seeing eye to eye, eventually leading to the team's disbandment.

After serving time as an agent with the Team 7 government strike force, Canary (Dinah Lance) went solo. She changed her name to Black Canary and gained employment at the Iceberg Casino to break up a deal between the Penguin and terrorist organization Basilisk. During this operation she met Starling and Batgirl, who would later join forces with her as the Birds of Prey.

"...Nobody on this team has a squeaky-clean soul."

Strix was brought onto the team by Batgirl

Black Canary relished serving on a new team

Batgirl took over as leader after Black Canary

Batgirl eventually disbanded the Birds

110

THOMAS WAYNE

ALLY

VITAL STATS

Full Name: Thomas Wayne

Occupation: Surgeon, philanthropist

Height: 6ft 2in

Weight: 210 lbs

Base: Gotham City

Allies: Martha and Bruce Wayne, Alfred and Jarvis Pennyworth, Lucius Fox

Foes: Joe Chill, the Court of Owls

POWERS AND ABILITIES

Highly skilled surgeon; powerful connections in the business world; amateur mechanic and inventor; extremely intelligent and loving father.

THE LAST NIGHT

Thomas and Martha Wayne's fate was sealed the night they took their son to a screening of The Mark of Zorro in Gotham City. After the film, they were shot dead by Joe Chill during a botched robbery.

Thomas Wayne was a loving husband and father. Born into a wealthy family, Thomas created quite a career for himself as a surgeon. Though he was killed when his son Bruce was just a boy, he had nevertheless created many memories with his son, including showing Bruce a Witch's Eye, a hi-tech visual mapping device that later helped inspire the creation of the Batman.

> **"What do you love about Gotham, Bruce?"**

Hat bears logo similar to Robin's

Wears casual attire in spare time when tinkering with mechanics

Doted on his son, often giving gifts

MARTHA WAYNE

ALLY

VITAL STATS

Full Name: Martha Wayne

Occupation: Mother, philanthropist

Height: 5ft 4in

Weight: 108 lbs

Base: Gotham City

Allies: Thomas and Bruce Wayne, Alfred and Jarvis Pennyworth

Foes: Joe Chill, the Court of Owls

POWERS AND ABILITIES

Empathetic philanthropist; powerful contacts in Gotham City's most elite social circles, partially due to Kane family name (Martha's maiden name); intelligent and giving mother.

MOTHER OF INNOVATION

Martha Wayne, a civic-minded woman, was upset at the state of Gotham City's education system. To fix the problem, she created a new school for Gotham City's underprivileged, despite receiving threats from the mayor's office.

A loving mother to Bruce Wayne, Martha Wayne was a philanthropist who stood up to Gotham City's corrupt mayor's office, not knowing it was backed by the violent, secret organization, the Court of Owls. The Court of Owls caused Martha to have a car "accident," and her loyal butler Jarvis Pennyworth was killed by a Talon assassin as well.

"You're the bravest boy in Gotham, Bruce."

While her life was full of tragedy, and would soon end thanks to Joe Chill, Martha spent much of her short life doting on her son, Bruce.

ALAN WAYNE

VITAL STATS

Full Name: Alan Wayne

Occupation: Railroad tycoon, socialite and investor

Height: 5ft 11in

Weight: 171 lbs

Base: Gotham City

Allies: Catherine Wayne, Theodore Cobblepot, Edward Elliot, Cameron Kane, Amadeus Arkham

Foes: The Court of Owls, Nicholas and Bradley Gates

POWERS AND ABILITIES

Influential Gotham City socialite with powerful connections; extremely wealthy and intelligent.

DEATH OF THE FATHER

In 1922, Alan Wayne was hold captivo in tho Court of Owls's underground labyrinth. When he emerged from the sewers, he ran straight into the arms of police officers before being killed by a Talon assassin.

Alan Wayne was the son of Judge Solomon Wayne, one of Gotham City's founders. Solomon had hired architect Cyrus Pinkney to build the city's first tall buildings and now Alan wanted to build even more. He hired architect brothers Nicholas and Bradley Gates to enhance the city's skyline, including building Wayne Tower. Alan was later killed by a Talon of the Court of Owls.

Alan, Bruce Wayne's great, great grandfather, and his wife Catherine took an active role in Gotham City's social issues.

"They're...coming for me!"

HARVEY BULLOCK

VITAL STATS

Full Name: Harvey Bullock

Occupation: G.C.P.D. detective

Height: 5ft 10in

Weight: 248 lbs

Base: Gotham City

Allies: James Gordon, G.C.P.D., Renee Montoya, Batman

Foes: Anarky, the Joker's Daughter, Dr. Death

POWERS AND ABILITIES

Excellent detective; good fighter with street smarts; loyal friend to James Gordon; one of the few honest cops in Gotham City.

BULLOCK'S LAW

As a rookie police officer, Bullock worked with James Gordon on several cases, including the emergence of Dr. Death. As a detective, he's come into his own, and is respected throughout the G.C.P.D.

Harvey Bullock, who has been working for the G.C.P.D. since the infamous citywide blackout, is one of Gotham City's clean cops, even if his appearance doesn't quite match his resumé. While he and Batman don't always see eye to eye, Bullock often worked with the Dark Knight, and now teams with the Dark Knight's successor, James Gordon, as head of Batman's task force team.

"I don't trust anyone... except you, Jimbo."

Harvey trained G.C.P.D. officer Renee Montoya and they became friends—before she moved to Blüdhaven. She has since returned.

RENEE MONTOYA

VITAL STATS

Full Name: Renee Montoya

Occupation: G.C.P.D. detective

Height: 5ft 8in

Weight: 144 lbs

Base: Gotham City

Allies: Harvey Bullock, Batman, James Gordon, Batwoman

Foes: Detective Nancy Yip, the Joker's Daughter

POWERS AND ABILITIES

Highly trained police detective; trained by Harvey Bullock; experienced fighter with good hand-to-hand combat skills.

A QUESTION OF ETHICS

While Renee Montoya has proven herself an honest police officer and fiercely loyal to other good cops, she's not above the occasional bar brawl. Especially when those she's trading punches with are known criminals.

In the Gotham City Police Department, it can often be hard to find cops on the right side of the law. While things have improved over the years thanks to James Gordon, that wasn't always the case. Corruption was rife in the department when Renee Montoya first started out, but she was determined to make a difference, aided and abetted by her instructor, Harvey Bullock.

"...you know how sacred partnerships are."

Back in Gotham City after years in Blüdhaven, Montoya wanted to root out corruption, and found an enemy in Detective Nancy Yip.

JAMES GORDON

VITAL STATS

Full Name: James W. Gordon

Occupation: Deputized vigilante, former police commissioner

Height: 5ft 9in

Weight: 168 lbs

Base: Gotham City

Allies: Batman, the Batman Family, Batgirl, G.C.P.D.

Foes: The Joker, Mr. Bloom, James Gordon, Jr.

POWERS AND ABILITIES

Extremely physically fit; natural leader; expertise in police procedure; former marine; robotic suit armed with crime-fighting equipment.

BATMAN 2.0

After the real Batman seemingly died, James Gordon stepped up to fill the role as a fully deputized agent of the law. Wearing a Batsuit inside a giant bat-themed robot suit, the 46-year-old does his best to fill Batman's shoes.

James Gordon worked his way up the chain of command at the Gotham City Police Department, fighting corruption at every turn. He eventually became commissioner, but was framed for murder and incarcerated. Gordon's job was not waiting for him when he was exonerated. However, he accepted an offer from Geri Powers to become the G.C.P.D.'s official Batman instead.

Haircut harks back to his days as a Marine

Shaved mustache to resemble Batman

Highly trained fighter

Got back in shape to become Batman

"Sometimes, you just have to get out and walk the beat."

THE JUSTICE LEAGUE

VITAL STATS

Team Name: The Justice League

Base: Watchtower satellite in Earth's orbit

Allies: Black Lightning, the Teen Titans, Black Canary

Foes: Darkseid, Anti-Monitor, the Crime Syndicate

Members:
Batman, Superman, Wonder Woman, Aquaman, Green Lantern (Hal Jordan), the Flash, Cyborg, Shazam, Power Ring, Martian Manhunter (former), Firestorm (former), Element Woman (former), Atomica (traitor), Lex Luthor, Captain Cold

NEW PARTNERSHIPS

It took some time for the founding Justice League members to trust one another. Some members, like Batman and Superman, began working together as partners outside of their Justice League missions.

The Justice League first formed when the other-dimensional tyrant Darkseid attempted to conquer Earth. Batman, Wonder Woman, Superman, Green Lantern, Cyborg, Aquaman, and the Flash successfully fought back, and decided to team up to battle other large-scale threats. Their roster has changed a few times, but they remain unwavering in their mission.

"You can call us... the Super Seven!"

The Justice League inducted "reformed" villains, Lex Luthor and Captain Cold, into their ranks after Luthor helped defeat the Crime Syndicate.

SUPERMAN

VITAL STATS

Real Name: Clark Kent, Kal-El

Occupation: Hero, reporter

Height: 6ft 3in

Weight: 235 lbs

Base: Metropolis

Allies: The Justice League, Steel, Supergirl, Superboy

Foes: Lex Luthor, Doomsday, Parasite, Darkseid

POWERS AND ABILITIES

Super-strength; super-speed; superhuman reflexes, senses, durability, and endurance; flight; heat vision; X-ray vision; freeze breath; solar flare; extremely intelligent; access to advanced Kryptonian technology; powers derived from Earth's yellow sun.

BREAK THE CHAINS
Superman is a match for any hero or villain. Green Lantern quickly learned this fact during the formation of the Justice League, when he tried and failed to restrain the Man of Steel with green energy constructs.

Baby Kal-El was rocketed to Earth when his planet, Krypton, exploded. Discovered by the Kent family, the infant was renamed Clark. As he matured, Clark discovered that Earth's yellow sun gave him awesome abilities. He soon put these powers to use in order to protect his adopted city of Metropolis as the ultimate Super Hero, Superman.

"Treat people right or expect a visit from me."

Kryptonian costume was found on alien conqueror Brainiac's ship

S-Shield is the symbol of his Kryptonian family

Superman's cape is indestructible

CLARK KENT

VITAL STATS

Full Name: Clark Kent, Kal-El

Occupation: Hero, reporter

Height: 6ft 3in

Weight: 235 lbs

Base: Metropolis

Allies: Lois Lane, Jimmy Olsen, Perry White, Bruce Wayne

Foes: Lex Luthor, Doomsday, Parasite, Darkseid

POWERS AND ABILITIES

Extremely intelligent; access to contacts from the world of journalism; mild-mannered persona created to deflect attention; excellent investigative skills.

SEEKER OF TRUTH

Beginning his career at the *Daily Star*, Clark Kent wrote intriguing and fearless exposés. He befriended the wealthy Jimmy Olsen in the process, as well as his longtime crush, another ace reporter, Lois Lane.

Everybody knows that Clark Kent grew up in Smallville, Kansas, and was raised by Jonathan and Martha Kent. But for years, Clark hid the fact that he is an alien from the distant planet Krypton. Clark was sent to Earth by his birth parents, Jor-El and Lara, when his planet was destroyed. Clark dedicates his career to truth as a reporter for the *Daily Planet*.

"I've waited my whole life for this."

Since most people don't think Superman has time for a secret life, his idea of hiding in plain sight, behind a pair of glasses, works perfectly.

WONDER WOMAN

VITAL STATS

Real Name: Diana

Occupation: Hero, queen, God of War

Height: 6ft

Weight: 165 lbs

Base: Themyscira

Allies: Superman, Orion, the Justice League

Foes: Cheetah, Circe, the First Born

POWERS AND ABILITIES

Godly blood grants her super-strength, endurance, and agility; power of flight; Bracelets of Victory can deflect bullets; expert fighter and strategist; Lasso of Truth forces others to tell the truth; extremely wise and empathetic.

HEAR HER ROAR

Wonder Woman has occasionally changed her armor, but always retains the "star" iconography that represents her family lineage. An emissary of peace, she is also a true warrior at heart.

Diana is the daughter of the god Zeus and Hippolyta, the ruler of Themyscira, an island of female warriors called the Amazons. Diana grew up a princess completely isolated from the rest of the world. When a pilot named Steve Trevor crashed on Themyscira, Diana learned of the outside world and soon traveled there as her people's representative and a true Super Hero—Wonder Woman.

"It's a big, strange, and wondrous universe."

Armor forged by god Hephaestus

Tiara a sign of regal lineage

Bracelets of Victory can produce blades

Flexible armor for ease of movement

Lasso can be used to attack or defend

AQUAMAN

VITAL STATS

Real Name:
Arthur Curry

Occupation: Hero, king
of Atlantis

Height: 6ft 1in

Weight: 325 lbs

Base: Atlantis

Allies: Mera, the Justice
League, the Others

Foes: Black Manta, Ocean
Master, the Trench

POWERS AND ABILITIES

Can breathe underwater;
can communicate with and
control sea life; ruler of
underwater kingdom of
Atlantis; super-strength;
trained fighter and natural
leader; swims incredibly fast.

FISH OUT OF WATER
Batman and Aquaman have fought
side-by-side on many missions as part
of the Justice League. The two have
also teamed up as partners on occasion,
including the time they battled Ra's al
Ghūl on a remote island in the Pacific.

Body can bear
pressures of
the deep

Blond hair rare
in Atlantis

Wears
scale-like
uniform

Carries
trident to
use as
weapon

Arthur Curry was born to a
lighthouse keeper and an Atlantean
queen, and raised on land when his
mother returned to the sea. Thanks
to his ability to breathe underwater
and communicate with sea life, Arthur
became known as Aquaman when he
was a young man. The rightful king of
Atlantis, he uses his abilities to fight
for creatures on land and in the ocean.

*"So who's in charge
here? I vote me."*

GREEN LANTERN

VITAL STATS

Real Name: Harold (Hal) Jordan

Occupation: Hero

Height: 6ft 2in

Weight: 186 lbs

Base: Mobile, Coast City

Allies: The Justice League, Green Lantern Corps

Foes: Sinestro, Red Lanterns, Black Hand

POWERS AND ABILITIES

Expert pilot; natural leader; Green Lantern ring can create physical manifestations of anything its user imagines; it also allows for flight, force fields, and space travel, and can impart encyclopedic knowledge to its wearer.

EMERALD KNIGHT

Green Lantern and Batman first met during Darkseid's invasion of the Earth. Hal Jordan was surprised to learn that the Dark Knight possessed no special powers, and was simply Bruce Wayne in an armored uniform.

As a child, Hal Jordan idolized his pilot father, who died in a plane crash. Hal grew up to be just like his dad, overcoming his fear of flying and finding work at Ferris Airlines. When Abin Sur, a member of the galactic peacekeepers known as the Green Lanterns, crashed his spaceship on Earth, his magical ring chose Hal to replace Abin Sur as the newest member of the Green Lanterns.

Ring creates Hal's mask and uniform

Responsible for protecting space sector 2814

Green power ring creates anything Hal can imagine

"You're not just some guy in a bat costume, are you?"

GREEN LANTERN

VITAL STATS

Real Name: John Stewart
Occupation: Hero
Height: 6ft 1in
Weight: 210 lbs
Base: Mobile
Allies: Green Lantern Corps, Hal Jordan, Kilowog
Foes: Red Lantern Corps, Larfleeze, Sinestro Corps

POWERS AND ABILITIES

Expert architect; military training; natural leader; Green Lantern ring can create physical manifestations of anything its user imagines; it also allows for flight, force fields, and space travel, and can impart encyclopedic knowledge to its wearer.

THE LOGICAL LANTERN

John Stewart is a military man and a former architect. As such, he thinks logically and precisely. While some of his fellow Green Lanterns may conjure fanciful objects with their rings, John keeps his constructs efficient.

The son of a political activist, John Stewart grew up learning to fight for what's right – peacefully. He left home in Detroit, Michigan, to join the Marines, and helped with the relief effort during the superstorm that caused Gotham City's blackout. But after falling out with his superiors, John was honorably discharged, only to be enlisted in a greater army, the Green Lantern Corps.

> *"This is the end of the road...just not for me."*

As a member of the intergalactic peacekeeping force, the Green Lantern Corps, John Stewart has finally found his purpose in life.

CYBORG

VITAL STATS

Real Name: Victor Stone

Occupation: Hero, scientist

Height: 6ft 5in

Weight: 385 lbs

Base: Detroit, Michigan

Allies: The Justice League, the Metal Men, S.T.A.R. Labs

Foes: Grid, the Crime Syndicate, Darkseid

POWERS AND ABILITIES

Cybernetic body allows for enhanced endurance, durability, agility, speed, and strength; can tap into world grid allowing internet access; computer and robotics expert; adept hacker; naturally athletic and intelligent; hi-tech weapons include white-noise blaster.

WORK IN PROGRESS

Cyborg is a founder of the Justice League, and was its youngest member until Shazam joined. After being attacked by the artificial life form known as Grid, Victor completely upgraded his cybernetic body.

A star football player in high school, Victor Stone was at odds with his father, who wanted Vic to pursue education over athletics. When Darkseid invaded Earth, Vic was mortally wounded, saved only when his father subjected him to an experimental cybernetic bonding process, turning him into a cyborg. Vic put his advanced artificial body to use, becoming a hero.

"What am I?"

Can access internet with a mere thought

Robotic body is incredibly durable

Favors white noise blasts of energy

SUPERGIRL

VITAL STATS

Real Name: Kara Zor-El

Occupation: Hero

Height: 5ft 5in

Weight: 120 lbs

Base: Mobile

Allies: Superman, Superboy, the Justice League United, Steel

Foes: Jochi, Silver Banshee, H'el

POWERS AND ABILITIES

Super-strength; super-speed; superhuman reflexes, durability, senses, and endurance; flight; heat vision; freeze breath; X-ray vision; access to advanced Kryptonian technology; powers derived from Earth's yellow sun.

WORLD'S FINEST

In order to defeat the threat of the alien Jochi, Superman and Batman had to pick two champion allies to compete in Warworld's deadly gladiatorial arena. Superman chose Steel and Supergirl and Batman chose Red Hood and Batgirl.

Kara Zor-El came from a prestigious family who lived in Argo City, one of the biggest metropolises on planet Krypton. Her scientist father, Zor-El, was Jor-El's brother. As Jor-El built a rocket ship to allow his baby Kal-El to escape Krypton's destruction, Zor-El created an escape pod for his daughter. Kara found her way to Earth and adopted the guise of Supergirl.

"You have to trust me to find my own way."

Like Clark Kent, she has freeze breath

Wears the El family S-Shield

Can fly at high speeds

THE FLASH

VITAL STATS

Real Name: Barry Allen

Occupation: Hero, forensic scientist

Height: 5ft 11in

Weight: 179 lbs

Base: Central City

Allies: The Justice League, Green Lantern, Iris West

Foes: Captain Cold, Mirror Master, Heatwave, Captain Boomerang

POWERS AND ABILITIES

Draws super-speed powers from an extradimensional Speed Force energy; extremely intelligent; well-versed in police procedure and detection; skilled crime scene investigator.

SPEED BUMPS

The Flash has gathered his own Rogues Gallery over the years, from villains like Heatwave, to murderers like the Keystone Killer. As the Flash, and as a crime scene investigator, he does his best to protect his city.

When Barry Allen was a boy, his mother died, and his father was arrested as the culprit. Desperate to get to the truth, Barry studied forensics, and later became a criminologist for the police. One night, a bolt of lightning struck a shelf of chemicals, splashing them onto Allen, giving him the power to move at fantastic speeds as the Flash.

Designed his own flame-colored costume

Costume can shrink small enough to fit inside a ring

Speed causes lightning to trail off behind him

"No matter what—I'll never stop chasing the truth."

MARTIAN MANHUNTER

VITAL STATS

Real Name: J'onn J'onzz

Occupation: Hero

Height: 6ft 7in

Weight: 250 lbs

Base: Mobile

Allies: The Justice League of America, the Justice League, Stormwatch, the Justice League United

Foes: The Crime Syndicate, the Secret Society

POWERS AND ABILITIES

Super-strength; super-speed; superhuman agility and endurance; invisibility; shape-shifting powers; flight; telepathy; Martian vision; able to pass through solid objects; highly intelligent and determined; natural leader.

SUPER-MANHUNTER

The Martian Manhunter is one of the most powerful Super Heroes. Possessing most of the abilities of Superman, J'onn's shape-shifting, telepathy, and invisibility powers give him a huge advantage in any fight.

The people of Mars lived a connected life, communicating with each other through their thoughts. When J'onn J'onzz became their leader, he journeyed to another world to experience the feeling of being alone. When he returned he found Mars aflame. Believing he was the planet's sole survivor, he traveled to Earth to use his powers for good as the Martian Manhunter.

"My friends call me J'onn..."

Can communicate with others by thought

Green skin a sign of Martian heritage

Costume can shape-shift with his flesh

Body can pass through solid objects

LEX LUTHOR

VITAL STATS

Full Name: Lex Luthor
Occupation: CEO of LexCorp, criminal
Height: 6ft 2in
Weight: 210 lbs
Base: Metropolis
Allies: Captain Cold, the Justice League, Mercy Graves, Brainiac
Foes: Superman, the Crime Syndicate, Batman

POWERS AND ABILITIES

Near unparalleled intellect; armored flight suit equipped with hi-tech weaponry and defenses; suit grants him superhuman strength and speed.

INJUSTICE FOR ALL

After convincing the world he was a true hero by playing a major part in the defeat of the Crime Syndicate, Lex Luthor rallied public support to become a member of the Justice League.

Lex Luthor first met Superman whilst working with the United States government and the alien entity known as Brainiac. Wishing to be mankind's savior against the alien threat Superman presented, he helped capture and experiment on the Kryptonian hero but Superman escaped. Luthor has maintained a vendetta against Superman ever since.

Genius-level intellect and business savvy

Clothes suit his luxurious lifestyle

Dresses in business attire, when not in hero costume

"I'm a changed man, Superman."

THE JOKER

VITAL STATS

Real Name: Unknown
Occupation: Criminal
Height: 6ft 5in
Weight: 192 lbs
Base: Gotham City
Allies: Harley Quinn,
the Joker's Daughter,
the Red Hood Gang
Foes: Batman, the Batman
Family, James Gordon

POWERS AND ABILITIES

Insanity causes unpredictable
behavior; agile and a
relentless fighter; twisted
genius mind with expertise in
chemistry, brilliant strategist;
lacks moral code; employs
clown-themed weapons;
Venom gives his victims
permanent grins.

KILLER CLOWN FROM GOTHAM CITY

The Joker considers himself Batman's
arch-enemy, and is virtually obsessed
with the hero and his team. During his
career, he has temporarily paralyzed
Batgirl and killed Jason Todd, and even
severed Alfred's hand.

While his true identity remains a
mystery, the Joker is believed to have
been the criminal known as Red Hood
One, the man in charge of the Red
Hood Gang. That chapter of his life
ended when Batman took down his
organization and knocked the criminal
into a vat of chemicals. The Joker
survived, albeit with severely altered
features, including a damaged mind.

*"Just think of the great times
we've had...and smile!"*

Uses razor-
sharp playing
cards as
weapons

Hair dyed green
from chemical
exposure

Trademark
purple suit
with clashing
shirt and tie

Employs deadly
"jokes" like acid-
squirting flowers

HARLEY QUINN

ROGUE

VITAL STATS

Real Name: Dr. Harleen Quinzel

Occupation: Criminal, landlord, roller derby participant

Height: 5ft 7in

Weight: 115 lbs

Base: Coney Island, Brooklyn, New York

Allies: The Joker, Suicide Squad, Poison Ivy, Scarecrow

Foes: Batman, the Batman Family

POWERS AND ABILITIES

Insanity causes unpredictability; agile and capable fighter; employs dozens of clown-themed weapons and lackeys; often uses giant hammer as a weapon.

LEFT HER HEART IN GOTHAM CITY

Putting Gotham City and her love affair with the Joker behind her, Harley Quinn moved to Coney Island and set up shop as a landlord, taking part in roller derbies.

Harley Quinn was a Gotham University graduate who began working at Arkham Asylum. To gain the inmates' trust, she dyed her hair two-toned and posed as a patient. The Joker saw through her ruse, and Harley found herself falling in love with him. They escaped Arkham, and the Joker threw her into a vat of chemicals to bleach her skin and cement their relationship.

"Oh, Mistah J…"

Enjoys the violence of roller derby

Adept at using trademark giant hammer

Skin bleached white thanks to the Joker

Not averse to using traditional guns

THE PENGUIN

VITAL STATS

Real Name: Oswald Chesterfield Cobblepot

Occupation: Crime boss, owner of the Iceberg Casino

Height: 5ft 2in

Weight: 175 lbs

Base: Gotham City

Allies: Lark, Catwoman, Mr. Toxic, Hypnotic, Mr. Combustible

Foes: Batman, the Batman Family, Black Canary

POWERS AND ABILITIES

Master strategist; brilliant criminal mind; employs a variety of trick umbrellas; major underworld connections.

OLD ENEMIES

Batman and the Penguin have a long history, going back to a time before either of them had adopted their animal-themed names. Batman often takes advantage of the Penguin's extensive criminal ties, scaring information out of the villain.

White gloves coordinate with the spats on his shoes

Physical features resemble a penguin

Weapons are concealed in his umbrellas

Agile and violent despite his size

Oswald Chesterfield Cobblepot hails from one of Gotham City's oldest and most influential families, albeit a corrupt one. Determined to climb to the top of the heap, Oswald continued his family's legacy, dealing in illegal weapons. Now known as the Penguin, he rose to power in Gotham City's underworld, becoming a feared crime boss and owner of the Iceberg Casino.

"Almost everything went according to plan, little birdie."

SCARECROW

VITAL STATS

Real Name: Dr. Jonathan Crane

Occupation: Criminal, former psychiatrist and college professor

Height: 6ft

Weight: 140 lbs

Base: Gotham City

Allies: The Secret Society, Professor Pyg, Merrymaker, Harley Quinn, Mr. Freeze

Foes: Batman, the Batman Family

POWERS AND ABILITIES

Near genius intellect; brilliant chemist and psychiatrist; crafts fear gas that causes victims to live their worst nightmares.

KNIGHT TERRORS

Scarecrow is obsessed with fear, taking every opportunity to experiment on his favorite subject, Batman. Using his "fear toxin," he has forced the Dark Knight to relive his tragic past—but Batman triumphs over his inner demons.

As a boy, Jonathan Crane's father carried out twisted experiments that tested the emotion of fear. Despite this scary experience, Jonathan followed in his father's footsteps, studying fear as a professor at university. Eventually, his own cruel experiments led to him being fired, which was when he adopted the role of the deadly Scarecrow.

Fabric mask with sewn-up mouth

Costume rigged to dispense fear gas

Adopted the name Scarecrow after being compared to one

"I'm the bogeyman."

THE RIDDLER

VITAL STATS

Real Name: Edward Nygma
Occupation: Criminal, former Wayne Enterprises employee
Height: 6ft 1in
Weight: 183 lbs
Base: Gotham City
Allies: Arkham Rogues
Foes: Batman, the Batman Family

POWERS AND ABILITIES

Genius-level intellect; expert at creating riddles and death traps; computer and electronics whiz; not above cheating to win a fight.

RIDDLE ME THIS

Obsessed with riddles from a young age, the Riddler began his campaign of crime by taking Gotham City hostage. Not only did the villain shut off Gotham City's power, but he also would have obliterated the city entirely, if not for Batman's intervention.

Edward Nygma originally worked as an advisor for Bruce Wayne's uncle, Philip Kane, at Wayne Enterprises. Even more corrupt than his employer, Nygma met the young Bruce Wayne soon after Bruce's return to Gotham City, and challenged him with a series of riddles. Following a falling out with Kane, Nygma became the Riddler— one of Batman's trickiest opponents.

> *"It's not a mystery you're dealing with here. It's a riddle."*

Bowler hat has replaced his old fedora

Trick cane loaded with remote technology

Trademark green suit

POISON IVY

VITAL STATS

Real Name: Pamela Lillian Isley

Occupation: Criminal, eco-terrorist

Height: 5ft 8in

Weight: 115 lbs

Base: Gotham City

Allies: Harley Quinn, Clayface, the Justice League United

Foes: Batman, the Batman Family, the Birds of Prey

POWERS AND ABILITIES

Controls and manipulates growth of plants; immune to toxins and poisons; produces pheromones that cause others to fall into her control; poisonous kiss; highly adept at botany and chemistry.

TANGLED IN IVY

Poison Ivy and Batman have clashed frequently, but they first butted heads when Isley worked briefly for Wayne Enterprises. She was fired for developing a mind-controlling pheromone that Bruce Wayne found immoral.

As a girl, Pamela Isley was adept at chemistry and developed a deadly toxin in her mother's garden that she could deliver to her enemies with a kiss. When she was accidentally doused with an experimental plant-based serum during a struggle in her lab, she gained the ability to communicate with nature. She soon set out to exploit that power as the eco-terrorist, Poison Ivy.

"Are you scared, little mammal?"

Can "speak" to plants and control them

Highly intelligent, with a mind for chemistry

Body changes with seasons like a true plant

Wears plant-based living costume

TWO-FACE

VITAL STATS

Real Name: Harvey Dent

Occupation: Criminal, former District Attorney

Height: 6ft

Weight: 182 lbs

Base: Gotham City

Allies: The Secret Society, Gilda Dent

Foes: Batman, the Batman Family, Erin McKillen

POWERS AND ABILITIES

Cunning strategist; expert knowledge of law and police procedure; split personality causes extreme unpredictability.

TWO SIDES OF THE SAME COIN

Harvey Dent and his old friend Bruce Wayne have become enemies as Two-Face and Batman. With a flip of his special coin, Two-Face lets luck dictate his every decision—good or evil.

Gotham City's District Attorney,

Harvey Dent, led a promising life as the city's golden boy. But when he crossed Erin McKillen of the organized crime family known as the McKillen Clan, his life changed forever. Erin took revenge upon Harvey and his family. The trauma of this tragic event released Harvey's dark side, and he took on the persona of the criminal Two-Face.

Handsome features are now forever marred

Wears two-toned clothing

Scarred two-headed coin to match his face

> **"Chance *trumps* choice every second of every day."**

BANE

VITAL STATS

Real Name: Unknown
Occupation: Criminal
Height: 6ft 8in
Weight: 350 lbs (425 lbs on Venom)
Base: Gotham City
Allies: Santa Prisca mercenaries
Foes: Batman, the Batman Family, Batwoman

POWERS AND ABILITIES

Extremely intelligent with an iron-clad will; brilliant strategist; skilled hand-to-hand fighter; enhanced strength, durability, weight, and endurance due to use of super-steroid Venom.

BREAKING BAT

Bane lives with one goal in mind: to break the Batman. Bane had heard legends of the Dark Knight while in his native country of Santa Prisca, and yearned to conquer the seemingly untamable Gotham City and its dark protector.

Always equipped with Venom supply

Venom injected directly into head

Huge exterior can overshadow brilliant mind

Often leads army of Santa Prisca soldiers

Born in the corrupt nation of Santa Prisca, the boy who would become Bane grew up in its cruelest prison, Pena Duro, becoming a hardened yet well-read man. The prison doctors injected him with a powerful steroid called Venom. Not only did the steroid work, it gave Bane the strength he needed to escape and set his sights on Gotham City.

"Only when I'm dead do I intend to rest."

CLAYFACE

VITAL STATS

Real Name: Basil Karlo

Occupation: Criminal, former actor

Height: Varies

Weight: Varies

Base: Gotham City

Allies: Poison Ivy, the Unknowns, Batwoman

Foes: Batman, the Batman Family

POWERS AND ABILITIES

Made of living clay that can bend and shape to his will; able to impersonate others by taking their exact shape and DNA; highly skilled actor.

IMPRESSIONABLE

While Clayface has primarily been an enemy of Batman, he briefly joined forces with Batwoman and a team called the Unknowns when he suffered from amnesia. He has since reverted to his criminal ways.

Basil Karlo was a famous actor, known primarily for his roles in horror films. However, when replaced as the lead in a movie, he turned to murder. His life began to take a strange path when he injected himself with a formula that altered his body completely, making him a shape-changer made of living clay. He became Clayface, one of Batman's most powerful enemies.

"...I ain't your daddy's Clayface!"

When Clayface takes on the forms of others, he now adopts their DNA. He can be anyone by just touching them; anyone but the man he once was.

RĀ'S AL GHŪL

VITAL STATS

Real Name: Unknown

Occupation: International terrorist

Height: 6ft 5in

Weight: 215 lbs

Base: 'Eth Alth'eban

Allies: The League of Assassins, Talia al Ghūl

Foes: Batman, Robin, the Batman Family

POWERS AND ABILITIES

Extremely long-life through his unprecedented access to the anti-aging Lazarus Pits; expert swordsman; highly skilled martial artist and fighter; genius intellect; master strategist.

HEIR APPARENT

Despite living for hundreds of years due to the Lazarus Pits, Rā's al Ghūl knows that he will die one day. He has tried hard to make Batman take on the role as his successor, but the Dark Knight constantly rejects his offer.

Legend tells of Rā's al Ghūl walking the Earth for the last 700 years. He adopted the name "The Demon's Head" after the death of his wife. Prolonging his own life through restorative Lazarus Pits, Rā's has amassed an entire League of Assassins with the goal of destroying the majority of the population in order to shape the world in his cruel image.

"My League of Assassins will tear this world apart..."

Speaks many different languages

Aging slowed thanks to Lazarus Pits

Ornate gold detailing

Wears regal clothing fit for a ruler

TALIA AL GHŪL

VITAL STATS

Full Name: Talia al Ghūl

Occupation: International terrorist

Height: 5ft 8in

Weight: 120 lbs

Base: Mobile

Allies: Rā's al Ghūl, Leviathan, Red Hood, the League of Assassins

Foes: Batman, Robin, the Batman Family, Batman, Inc.

POWERS AND ABILITIES

Access to huge terrorist networks; superb fighter and assassin; extremely intelligent with a mind for strategy; charismatic leader; worked her way into both Batman and Robin's hearts.

IN THE NAME OF THE FATHER

While she stayed by his side for years, Talia al Ghūl later parted ways with her father. She formed her own terrorist organization called Leviathan, and set out to destroy Batman once and for all

Talia al Ghūl is the daughter of the terrorist Rā's al Ghūl, and grew up learning the evil methods of being an assassin. When she met Batman, the two were instantly attracted to one another and had a short-lived romance that resulted in the birth of their son, Damian Wayne. While leading the criminal organization Leviathan, Talia was shot and presumably killed.

> ### "Look into the eye of the gorgon."

Uses laboratories for immoral experiments

Beauty causes some to drop their guard

Wears expensive regal attire

MR. FREEZE

VITAL STATS

Real Name: Dr. Victor Fries

Occupation: Criminal, former scientist

Height: 6ft

Weight: 190 lbs

Base: Gotham City

Allies: Starling, Scarecrow, Harley Quinn, Merrymaker, Professor Pyg

Foes: Batman, the Batman Family, the Birds of Prey, the Court of Owls

POWERS AND ABILITIES

Refrigerated suit gives him superhuman strength and endurance; developed quick-freeze technology in the form of freeze guns and grenades; genius-level intellect.

ICE IN HIS VEINS

With a body temperature of 23 degrees Fahrenheit, Victor Fries was fitted with special goggles to keep his eyes from freezing. He developed a refrigerated exoskeleton and an arsenal of cold weapons to become Mr. Freeze.

When Victor Fries was just a boy, his mother died in a frozen lake. As an adult, he took a job at Wayne Enterprises' cryogenics lab, where he focused on freezing bodies. He became obsessed with the frozen body of a woman he'd never met, Nora Fields. When Bruce Wayne closed his division, Fries lashed out, causing a lab accident that transformed him into Mr. Freeze.

"You don't understand what you're meddling with, Batman."

Mr. Freeze is obsessed with Nora Fields and believes they were married before she was frozen. He'll kill anyone that hampers finding her a cure.

KILLER CROC

VITAL STATS

Real Name: Waylon Jones

Occupation: Criminal

Height: 6ft 5in

Weight: 268 lbs

Base: Gotham City

Allies: Arsenal, Catwoman

Foes: Batman, the Batman Family, Bane

POWERS AND ABILITIES

Enhanced strength, durability, and endurance due to rare skin condition; excellent fighter with a history of wrestling alligators.

LURKING IN THE SEWERS

On the surface, Killer Croc can be perceived as simple muscle, but in the sewers he commands respect. Croc knows the underground inside and out, and has even ruled over tribes of vagabonds. He is known to them as King Croc.

Waylon Jones was raised by his Aunt Flowers in the poor neighborhood of Crown Point in Gotham City. Born with a skin condition that caused scale growth all over his body, Waylon knew no other life aside from one in a circus sideshow. Frustrated with his low pay and, after biting his employer while in a rage, Jones ventured into a life of crime as Killer Croc.

Teeth filed to sharp points

Extremely strong and muscular

Skin tough and difficult to pierce

"Death by Croc."

THE COURT OF OWLS

VITAL STATS

Team Name: The Court
of Owls
Base: Gotham City
Allies: Army of Talons and
fellow secret Owl members
Foes: Batman, Bane,
Talon (Calvin Rose),
Lincoln March

Notable Past Members:
Benjamin Orchard, John
Wycliffe, Maria Powers,
Joseph Powers, Sebastian
Clark, Lincoln March

GRIPPED BY TALONS
Batman mistakenly
suspected the Court of Owls
was behind his parents'
murder. He first encountered
the Court when he was
trapped in their labyrinth
beneath Gotham City, and he
barely managed to escape.

A cult as old as Gotham City itself, the
Court of Owls is a secret society of the
most nefarious order. Clandestinely
controlling politics and the evolution of
the city from behind closed doors, the
Court employs an elite army of Talons
—loyal assassins who murder their
enemies from the shadows. Batman
stopped a troubling resurgence, but
the Court is still alive in Gotham City.

*"...Beware the Court of Owls,
that watches all the time..."*

Members wear
owl masks to
hide identities

Children
brainwashed
at young age

Order members
are typically
society's richest

TALON

VITAL STATS

Real Name: William Cobb

Occupation: Assassin for the Court of Owls

Height: 6ft 3in

Weight: 220 lbs

Base: Gotham City

Allies: The Court of Owls

Foes: Batman, Dick Grayson, the Batman Family

POWERS AND ABILITIES

Expertly trained assassin; natural fighter and trained martial artist; superb at knife throwing; has healing ability and can be resurrected from the dead; long-lived and experienced.

CAPE VS. CLAW

When Bruce Wayne was targeted by Talon, Batman began investigating the Court of Owls. This led him to discover the Court's labyrinth, where he was forced to combat Cobb and just barely triumphed over him to escape.

William Cobb, one of the Court of Owls's finest Talon assassins, is the great-grandfather of Dick Grayson. Growing up poor on the streets of Gotham City in the early 1900s, Cobb was recruited into Haly's Circus where he became an expert knife handler. Cobb soon became a Talon for the Court of Owls, later offering his "gray son" to Haly's Circus for training.

"Bruce Wayne. The Court of Owls has sentenced you to die."

Uses owls and owl imagery to threaten

Wears owl-like enhanced goggles

Expert knife thrower

Each Talon wears a different uniform

MAN-BAT

VITAL STATS

Real Name: Dr. Kirk Langstrom

Occupation: Scientist and science teacher, acting head of S.H.A.D.E. Security

Height: 6ft 1in

Weight: 201 lbs

Base: Gotham City

Allies: Gotham Academy, S.H.A.D.E., the Outlaws

Foes: Batman, Bat-Queen, the Batman Family

POWERS AND ABILITIES

Serum transforms him into a monstrous Man-Bat with enhanced strength, speed, agility, and endurance, with capability of flight; genius-level intellect.

BAT VS. MAN

While Kirk's savagery as Man-Bat has put him at odds with Batman, he has recently found a way to control his transformations, now taking jobs at the clandestine operation S.H.A.D.E., as well as at Gotham Academy.

Dr. Kirk Langstrom is a noble scientist who wanted to find a cure for the deaf. He developed the Langstrom Atavistic Gene Recall Serum, but unfortunately it transformed its victims into hideous humanoid bat creatures. When a sample of the serum was stolen and unleashed on Gotham City, Kirk injected himself with an anti-virus. This cured the innocents but left Kirk as the sole remaining Man-Bat.

"I had to become the creature."

Combining several doses of his serum with a serum created by his wife, Langstrom can change into Man-Bat with only a thought.

MR. ZSASZ

VITAL STATS

Full Name: Victor Zsasz

Occupation: Criminal

Height: 5ft 8in

Weight: 150 lbs

Base: Gotham City

Ally: Emperor Blackgate

Foes: Batman, the Penguin, Merrymaker

POWERS AND ABILITIES

Deadly efficient murderer; excellent physical condition; mentally unstable and obsessed with murder; usually prefers using blades or knives.

DEATH TALLY

One of Gotham City's most dangerous and psychotic villains, Mr. Zsasz likes to keep a tally of his kills. For every person he murders, he carves a notch in his own flesh to remember them by.

Victor Zsasz has an addictive personality, and was therefore an easy mark when he gambled in the Penguin's Iceberg Casino. The heir to Zsasz Industries, Victor lost all his money thanks to the Penguin encouraging his love of gambling. Victor's mind snapped, and he embarked on a killing spree that continues to this day, despite Batman's efforts to stop him.

"The bird-man. This was all his doing. He gave me the knife."

While he usually prefers to work alone, Zsasz has been the willing pawn of Emperor Blackgate in the past, helping to spread the Man-Bat virus.

THE MAD HATTER

VITAL STATS

Real Name: Jervis Tetch

Occupation: Criminal

Height: 4ft 8in

Weight: 149 lbs

Base: Gotham City

Allies: Tweedledee, Tweedledum

Foes: Batman, Red Robin, Bluebird, Black Mask, Anarky

POWERS AND ABILITIES

Extremely intelligent; brilliant inventor and technician; uses drugged teas to enhance his own physical abilities; fanatically obsessed with Lewis Carroll's stories and poems; creations let him control the minds of others.

BATTLE OF THE MINDS

The Mad Hatter drinks a variety of drugged teas to give himself an advantage in a fight. Depending on the mixture, his teas can give him heightened pain tolerance or superhuman strength.

Obsessed with hats and Lewis Carroll's classic *Alice in Wonderland* stories, a young Jervis Tetch fell in love with his classmate, Alice. When she spurned him, he used testosterone enhancers to help his body grow, but instead developed violent tendencies. Years later, as the Mad Hatter, he uses his gift for invention to ensure that no one will ever reject him again.

"No one gets between me and my beloved!"

Hat contains mind control technology

Often quotes Carroll during encounters

Attire based on Lewis Carroll's Mad Hatter

DARKSEID

VITAL STATS

Real Name: Uxas

Occupation: Ruler of Apokolips

Height: 8ft 9in

Weight: 1,815 lbs

Base: Apokolips

Allies: Desaad, Kalibak, Granny Goodness, Parademons

Foes: The Justice League, Batman, Superman, Highfather, Orion

POWERS AND ABILITIES

Omega Effect eye beams can kill, resurrect, harm, or send victims hurtling through time; superhuman strength and endurance; commands armies of Parademons, elite soldiers, and a planet of minions.

GOD AMONG MEN

Darkseid had conquered many worlds before, including Earth-Two, a parallel dimension to the Earth of the Justice League. So when the League chased him off their planet, he swore revenge.

The planet Apokolips has been at war with its neighboring world New Genesis for years. Darkseid is the ruler of Apokolips and wants nothing less than to achieve mastery over death and rule the universe. To that end, he has clashed with the Justice League and Batman, when the Dark Knight traveled to Apokolips to rescue the body of the temporarily dead Damian Wayne.

"You came a long way to die."

Eyes produce devastating Omega Beams

Stone-like body can overpower even Superman

Towers over members of the Justice League

THE RED HOOD GANG

ROGUES

VITAL STATS

Team Name: The Red Hood Gang

Base: Gotham City

Allies: Fellow Red Hood members

Foes: Batman, G.C.P.D., the Penguin, the Falcone Family

Members:
Red Hood One (possibly the Joker), the original Red Hood One (Liam Distal), Philip Kane, dozens of mysterious members

A PLAGUE ON GOTHAM CITY

The citizens of Gotham City lived in fear during the Red Hood Gang's reign of terror. The well-dressed thugs robbed banks, destroyed buildings, and made the city streets unsafe. Most people were too afraid to stand up to the violent gang—but not Bruce Wayne.

When Bruce Wayne returned home from training abroad, Gotham City was plagued by the Red Hood Gang. Led by the notorious Red Hood One, the gang was taking over some of the Falcone gang's territory. Before he adopted his identity as Batman, Bruce opposed the gang, only to have them destroy his operations base near Crime Alley, almost killing him in the process.

"Gotham's Finest! Kill them all!"

After Bruce was injured by the Red Hood Gang, he realized he had to become more than a man to take them on—and so his Batman persona was born.

BLACK MASK

VITAL STATS

Real Name: Roman Sionis

Occupation: Criminal

Height: 6ft 1in

Weight: 195 lbs

Base: Gotham City

Allies: The False Face Society

Foes: Batman, the Mad Hatter

POWERS AND ABILITIES

Wears ebony mask that seems to give him telepathic and telekinetic powers; natural leader; expert strategist; capable hand-to-hand combatant; very intelligent; expert in torture techniques.

MASK VS. HAT

Black Mask's father's casket has long been one of the holy grails for the Mad Hatter, another of Batman's foes obsessed with mind control. This put the Hatter and Black Mask at odds, and made them natural rivals.

Uses mask to control False Face Society

Accustomed to wearing expensive clothes

Fancy suit juxtaposed with frightful mask terrifies foes

The rich yet disturbed heir to the Janus Cosmetics company, Roman Sionis was rumored to have played an active part in his parents' death when their home burned to the ground. Obsessed with masks, Roman carved his infamous black mask out of his father's coffin, later discovering that the casket was made of a strange material that gave him special abilities.

"Can't you see your mind is too weak to defend against my probe?!"

MAXIE ZEUS

VITAL STATS

Full Name: Maximilian Zeus

Occupation: Criminal

Height: 5ft 6in

Weight: 135 lbs

Base: Gotham City

Allies: Deacon Blackfire, Professor Milo, the Joker's Daughter

Foes: Batman, Batwing, the Batman Family

POWERS AND ABILITIES

Fit and athletic; capable hand-to-hand combatant; intelligent natural leader with a severe god complex; many connections in the business world and the criminal underworld.

THE POWER OF ZEUS

While staying in Arkham Asylum, Maxie Zeus was rendered near catatonic and felt nothing. This made him especially difficult to best in a fight, as the hero Batwing soon discovered firsthand.

For a time, Maxie Zeus was a successful crime boss in Gotham City. However, he began to lose his grip on reality and think of himself as a god, despite being bested by his enemy, the Batman. Later sentenced to a stay in Arkham Asylum, Zeus briefly hosted the spirit of Deacon Blackfire in his own body. This led to a battle with Batwing and the Spectre.

"Bow down to me, mortal."

Zeus was treated like the god he believed he was when he joined a cult intent on resurrecting Deacon Blackfire, whose spirit possessed his body.

HERETIC

ROGUE

VITAL STATS

Real Name: None

Occupation: Terrorist

Height: 7ft 4in

Weight: 345 lbs

Base: Mobile

Allies: Talia al Ghūl, Leviathan

Foes: Batman, Robin, the Batman Family

POWERS AND ABILITIES

Superhuman strength, endurance, and durability; weapons expert; master swordsman; excellent hand-to-hand combatant; seemingly unaffected by pain; wears protective armor that includes a jetpack to enable flight.

BORN TO KILL

The Heretic was meant to be Robin's replacement, one Talia made sure Damian was aware of before she cast him out of her family. The Heretic trained in Yemen and killed many superhumans in preparation for his role as Talia's ally.

Grown in a lab and hatched out of a whale carcass by Talia al Ghūl and her clandestine Leviathan organization, the Heretic was a grotesquely aged "brother" to Talia's son, Damian Wayne—also known as Robin. Desperate to prove his love to Talia, the Heretic served her, destroying anyone who threatened Leviathan, including, eventually, Damian himself.

"I watch. I listen. I learn. I am Batman now."

Underneath his robes, the Heretic wore Batman-styled armor. Despite his desire to please his mother, Talia hated the Heretic.

INDEX

Main entries are in **bold**.

ARTIST ACKNOWLEDGMENTS

This book contains material which has previously been published in the latest edition of *DC Comics: Batman Character Encyclopedia*, which illustrations from the following artists:

Christian Alamy, Juan Albarran, Oclair Albert, Rafael Albuquerque, Laura Alfred, Michael Alfred, Marlo Alquiza, Brad Anderson, Marc Andreyko, Joy Ang, Ulises Arreola, Mahmud Asrar, Michael Atiyeh, Tony Aviña, Matt Banning, Al Barrionuevo, Eddy Barrows, Jacob Bear, David Beaty, Tony Bedard, Ed Benes, Mariah Benes, Bengal, Ryan Benjamin, Marguerite Bennet, Joe Bennett, Rain Beredo, Lee Bermejo, W. Haden Blackman, Fernando Blanco, Blond, Roger Bonet, James Bonny, Brett Booth, Geraldo Borges, Andrei Bressan, Vera Brosgol, Jimmy Broxton, Brian Buccellato, Cullen Bunn, Riccardo Burchielli, Chris Burnham, Jim Calafiore, Greg Capullo, Juan Castro, Keith Champagne, Howard Chaykin, Clio Chiang, ChrisCross, June Chung, Vicente Cifuentes, Scott Clark, Andy Clarke, Ronan Cliquet, Becky Cloonan, Andre Coelho, Simon Coleby, David Cole, Amanda Conner, Will Conrad, Darwyn Cooke, Paul Cornell, Jorge Corona, Jeromy Cox, Wes Craig, Andrew Dalhouse, Federico Dallacchio, Tony S. Daniel, Marc Deering, Tom DeFalco, Werther Dell'Edera, Jesse Delperdang, Tom Derenick, Johnny Desjardins, Dan DiDio, Andy Diggle, Rachel Dodson, Terry Dodson, Jed Dougherty, Christian Duce, Dale Eaglesham, Scott Eaton, Gabe Eltaeb, Nathan Eyring, Jason Fabok, Nathan Fairbairn, Romulo Fajardo, Jr., Ray Fawkes, Raul Fernandez, Eber Ferreira, Julio Ferreira, Juan Ferreyra, Pascal Ferry, David Finch, Meredith Finch, Brenden Fletcher, Sandu Florea, Fabrizio Florentino, Jorge Fornes, Gary Frank, Derek Fridolfs, Richard Friend, Lee Garbett, Alex Garner, Javier Garrón, Sterling Gates, Dave Geraci, Drew Geraci, Ransom Getty, Sunny Gho, Keith Giffen, Jonathan Glapion, Adam Glass, Patrick Gleeson, Joel Gomez, Julius Gopez, Mick Gray, Justin Gray, Dan Green, Michael Green, Ig Guara, R.M. Guera, Andres Guinaldo, Scott Hanna, Chad Hardin, Joe Harris, James Harvey, Jeremy Haun, Rob Haynes, Doug Hazlewood, Daniel Henriques, Scott Hepburn, Meghan Hetrick, Hi-Fi Design, Kyle Higgins, David Hine, Bryan Hitch, Sandra Hope, Corin Howell, Adam Hughes, Ken Hunt, Rob Hunter, Gregg Hurwitz, Frazer Irving, Mark Irwin, Jack Jadson, Al Jaffee, Mikel Janín, Georges Jeanty, Paul Jenkins, Jorge Jimenez, Jock, Geoff Johns, Staz Johnson, Mike Johnson, Henrik Jonsson, Ruy José, Juancho, Dan Jurgens, John Kalisz, Jon Katz, Karl Kerschi, Karl Kesel, Tom King, Tyler Kirkham, Scott Kolins, Ales Kot, Andrew Kreisberg, Andy Kubert, Szymon Kudranski, Michel Lacombe, José Ladrönn, David Lafuente, Serge Lapointe, Ken Lashley, John Layman, Jae Lee, Jim Lee, Jay Leisten, Jeff Lemire, Rick Leonardi, Yishan Li, Rob Liefeld, LLC, Scott Lobdell, Jeph Loeb, Alvaro Lopez, David Lopez, Emilio Lopez, Aaron Lopresti, Lee Loughridge, Jorge Lucas, Ant Lucia, Emanuela Lupacchino, Doug Mahnke, Marcelo Maiolo, Guy Major, Alex Maleev, Francis Manapul, Leandro Manco, Clay Mann, Guillem March, Alitha Martinez, Allen Martinez, Alvaro Martinez, Stefano Martino, Christy Marx, José Marzan, Jr., Jason Masters, J.P. Mayer, Dave McCaig, Ray McCarthy, Trevor McCarthy, Scott McDaniel, Mike McKone, Lan Medina, Hermann Mejia, Javier Mena, Jaime Mendoza, Jesús Merino, Jonboy Meyers, Danny Miki, Romano Molenaar, Jorge Molina, Sula Moon, Stephen Mooney, Tomeu Morey, Moritat, Grant Morrison, Paul Mounts, Dustin Nguyen, Tom Nguyen, Fabian Nicieza, Ann Nocenti, Mike Norton, Kevin Nowlan, Sonia Oback, Patrick Olliffe, Guillermo Ortego, Andy Owens, Agustin Padilla, Greg Pak, Jimmy Palmiotti, Dan Panosian, Eduardo Pansica, Pete Pantazis, Yanick Paquette, Jeff Parker, Sean Parsons, Fernando Pasarin, Allen Passalaqua, Jason Pearson, Paul Pelletier, Pere Perez, Cris Peter, Will Pfeifer, Javier Piña, FCO Plascencia, Francis Portela, Howard Porter, Eric Powell, Joe Prado, Jack Purcell, Joe Quinones, Wil Quintana, Frank Quitely, Khary Randolph, Norm Rapmund, John Rauch, Sal Regla, Ivan Reis, Rod Reis, Cliff Richards, Tom Richmond, Jeremy Roberts, Roger Robinson, Kenneth Rocafort, Robson Rocha, Prentis Rollins, Alex Ross, Stéphane Roux, Felix Ruiz, Matt Ryan, Sean Ryan, Juan Jose Ryp, Jesús Saíz, Edgar Salazar, Tim Sale, Daniel Sampere, Rafa Sandoval, Derlis Santacruz, Trevor Scott, Tim Seeley, Emanuel Simeoni, Gail Simone, Alex Sinclair, Paulo Siqueira, Dan Slott, Brett Smith, Scott Snyder, Ben Sokolowski, Ryan Sook, Andrea Sorrentino, Chris Sotomayor, Peter Steigerwald, Cameron Stewart, Jeff Stokely, RC Stoodios, Karl Story, Carrie Strachan, Mico Suayan, Goran Sudzuka, Duane Swierczynski, Ardian Syaf, Phillip Tan, Babs Tarr, Jordi Tarragona, Ben Templesmith, Art Thibert, Frank Tieri, Marcus To, Peter Tomasi, Andy Troy, James Tynion IV, Ethan Van Sciver, Roberto Viacava, Dexter Vines, Alessandro Vitti, Joe Weems, Scott Williams, J.H. Williams III, Judd Winick, Ryan Winn, Marv Wolfman, Walden Wong, Jason Wright, Annie Wu, Matt Yackey, Craig Yeung, Richard Zajac, Patrick Zircher.

SENIOR EDITOR Victoria Taylor, and Cefn Ridout
PROJECT EDITOR Shari Last
EDITORS Laura Nickoll, Matt Jones, Clare Millar, and Rosie Peet
SENIOR DESIGNER Robert Perry
DESIGNERS Chris Gould, Pallavi Kapur, and David McDonald
DTP DESIGNERS Umesh Singh Rawat, Rajdeep Singh
PRE-PRODUCTION PRODUCER Kavita Varma
SENIOR PRODUCER Gary Batchelor
MANAGING EDITOR Sadie Smith
MANAGING ART EDITORS Ron Stobbart, Neha Ahuja
CREATIVE MANAGER Sarah Harland
PUBLISHER Julie Ferris
ART DIRECTOR Lisa Lanzarini
PUBLISHING DIRECTOR Simon Beecroft

READING CONSULTANT Linda B Gambrell
DESIGN AND ADDITIONAL TEXT Rich T Media
ADDITIONAL DESIGN Dynamo Limited

Dorling Kindersley would like to thank Josh Anderson, Benjamin Harper, and Amy Weingartner at Warner Bros. Global Publishing and Leah Tuttle at DC Entertainment. Thanks also to Vanessa Bird for the index, Joel Kempson, Lauren Nesworthy, Lisa Stock, and Chitra Subramanyam for editorial assistance, and Lisa Robb, Radhika Banerjee, and Ishita Chawla for design assistance.

First American Edition, 2016
Published in the United States by DK Publishing
345 Hudson Street, New York, New York 10014
DK, a Division of Penguin Random House LLC

Contains content previously published in *DK Adventures: Batman: Adventures of a Dark Knight* (2016), and *DC Comics: Batman Character Encyclopedia* (2016)

Page design Copyright © 2016 Dorling Kindersley Limited

001-299275-Jun/16

**A WORLD OF IDEAS:
SEE ALL THERE IS TO KNOW**